Human Roots

Buddhist Stories for Young Readers

Adapted &
Translated into English by
Dharma Realm Buddhist University,
Buddhist Text Translation Society
Talmage, California 1982

HUMAN ROOTS: Buddhist Stories for Young Readers

All the stories but one in this volume are true
accounts of past events involving Buddhas, Bodhisattvas, Arhats, sages, and other great beings.
They have been compiled from the Tripitaka, public
records, and historical accounts. The only exception is "WALKING STICK SUI," which is fiction
written by Kuo Lin (Nancy) Lethcoe as an offering
in accord with Dharma.

BUDDHIST TEXT TRANSLATION SOCIETY:

Adapted and compiled by Bhikshuni Heng Wen
Translated by Bhikshuni Heng Ch'ih and Upasika
    Kuo Ts'an (Terri) Nicholson
Edited by Upasika Kuo Tsai (Susan) Rounds
Certified by Venerable Abbot Hua & Bhikshuni Heng Tao
ISBN: 0-88139-500-5
Copyright © 1982 by the SINO-AMERICAN BUDDHIST
ASSOCIATION, DHARMA REALM BUDDHIST UNIVERSITY.

PRINTED IN THE UNITED STATES OF AMERICA
First printing: September 16, 1982, Anniversary
    of Earth Store Bodhisattva's Birthday
            1983 second printing
ACKNOWLEDGEMENTS:

drawings by Bhikshuni Heng Jieh,Upasika Kuo Kung Owen
cover calligraphy & design and typing by Shramanerika
    Heng Liang
proofing by Bhikshuni Heng Chu, Bh. Heng Hsien,
Bh. Heng Chia Bh. Heng Cheng, Kuo Tsai Rounds,
Kuo Lu Cole, Kuo Ts'an Nicholson,Kuo Chih Epstein
                ****

FOR INFORMATION AND BOOKSALES CONTACT:

GOLD MOUNTAIN MONASTERY, 1731-15th Street, San
    Francisco, Ca. 94103 (415) 861-9672 & 626-4204

GOLD WHEEL TEMPLE, 1728 West 6th Street, Los Angeles,
    California 90017   (213) 483-7497
                       (213) 258-6177
CITY OF TEN THOUSAND BUDDHAS, Box 217 Talmage, Ca.
    95481   (707) 462-0939
                *****

Buddhist Text Translation Society
Eight Regulations

A translator must free himself or herself from the motives of personal fame and reputation.

A translator must cultivate an attitude free from arrogance and conceit.

A translator must refrain from aggrandizing himself or herself and denigrating others.

A translator must not establish himself or herself as the standard of correctness and suppress the work of others with his or her faultfinding.

A translator must take the Buddha-mind as his or her own mind.

A translator must use the wisdom of the Selective Dharma Eye to determine true principles.

A translator must request the Elder Virtuous Ones of the ten directions to certify his or her translations.

A translator must endeavor to propagate the teachings by printing sutras, shastra texts, and vinaya texts when the translations are certified as being correct.

南無本師釋迦牟尼佛

Namo Shakyamuni Buddha

TABLE OF CONTENTS

Human
Roots

LION'S MILK

At the time when Shakyamuni Buddha was dwelling at the Garden of the Benefactor of Orphans and the Solitary, there were four brothers whose father died, leaving them with the family wealth. But the four could not agree on how to divide the wealth and were constantly fighting over who should get what. Unable to resolve their argument, they appealed to Shariputra to help them. Shariputra replied, "Fine, I have a teacher who is just and fair. Let me take you to him to see if your problem can be resolved." Shariputra's teacher, of course, was the Buddha.

The brothers agreed so they all went to where the Buddha was to try to get their problem straightened out. When the Buddha saw Shariputra and the four brothers coming, he smiled. They appealed to him to help them and he agreed, but instead of answering them directly, he told them this story:

"Once upon a time a king got very sick and was told he would die unless he took some medicine made out of lion's milk. Now the king didn't have any lion's milk, so he made this announcement throughout his kingdom: 'Whoever can secure some lion's milk and present it to the king will receive one of the princesses in marriage and will be made the king of a lesser country, endowed with servants and officials.'

"One poor hunter who heard the announcement decided to try his skill. He went high up into the mountains to a place which he knew was inhabited

-1-

by lions. There he set out some wine and raw meat and hid himself to wait. Sure enough, before long, along came a large lioness. When the beast found the wine and meat she ate and drank to her heart's content. As a result, she became drunk and sleepy and soon lay down for a nap. That was just what the hunter had hoped for and he took the opportunity to milk the lion.

"Having succeeded in his aim, he went back down the mountain and found a hotel where he could pass the night. Exhausted from his efforts, he soon fell into a deep sleep. Meanwhile, an Arhat came along and decided to spend the night beside the hotel. During the night, the Arhat saw six parts of the man's body quarrelling with each other, and the hunter had this dream: He dreamed his legs were boasting about getting the lion's milk all on their own. 'If I hadn't walked all the way up that mountain, he never could have gotten the milk.' But his arms set to quarrelling with his legs saying, 'Phooey on you. If I hadn't milked the lion, he never would have been able to get the milk out.' His ears joined the argument saying, 'Look, remember how it all began? If I hadn't heard that the king would offer his daughter and a kingdom for some lion's milk, he never would have gone off to hunt for one.' His eyes said, 'If I didn't see, none of the rest of you would ever be able to do anything. At that point his tongue spoke up and said, 'Silence, all of you. The merit will lie with me, you'll see.' But the reaction to the tongue's statement so outraged the legs, hands,

-2-

eyes and ears that the fuss they made woke the hunter. 'Well, anyway, I've got the lion's milk,' he commented.

"He set off early to go to the palace and when he reached it, he was given an audience with the king. But his tongue was just waiting for the right moment and it burst out, 'This isn't really lion's milk, it's donkey's milk,' it fairly shouted. The king was dismayed and then outraged. 'You come to waste my time with a donkey's milk?' he scolded. 'You shall be executed!'

"Remember the Arhat who had passed the night beside the hotel where the hunter had stayed? Well, he remembered the quarrel and knew that the tongue was just getting the best of the legs, the hands, the eyes and the ears. So he went to the King and explained the situation. 'Your Majesty, that really is lion's milk which that hunter brought you this morning.' And then he related the events he had witnessed. The King believed the Arhat, called forth the lion's milk, and had a medicine prepared. When he drank the lion's milk, he recovered from his illness. True to his word, he offered the hunter a princess in marriage and gave him a kingdom over which to govern."

When the Buddha finished relating this story he turned to the four brothers and said, "You see, it's not just brothers who fight among themselves. Even our own bodies fight all the time and cause a lot of trouble." The brothers understood the message and promised to drop their quarrel over their father's inheritance. In fact, they resolved

to leave the home life and shortly after certified
to Arhatship. Ananda could not understand why
these four brothers had responded so readily to
the Buddha's teaching and had been able to certify
to Arhatship so fast. Ananda asked the Buddha what
kind of merit and virtue these four had that en-
abled them to have this happen to them. The Buddha
told him, "At the time of Mwo Wen Buddha, Shariputra was a Bhikshu and these four people came and
joined together in making an offering of a Kashaya
sash to him. From the merit and virtue they accrued through that act of giving, they have now
been able to leave the home life and accomplish
Arhatship."

*Shariputra was a Bhikshu and these four people
came and joined together in making an offering
of a Kashaya (Precept sash) to him.*

THE BIG BEAR

One day a man went up into the mountains to gather firewood. But he lost his way, and then a heavy rainstorm hit. The more he wandered, the darker and more rainy it became and he was desperately hungry. Soon, all around him, he could hear the sounds of wild beasts. They sounded hungry, too. Once he caught a glimpse of a tiger and a lion and the sight scared him terribly. Eventually he found a cave and ducked into it, hoping for a little safety and perhaps a dry spot. But once in the cave, he turned around to find himself face to face with a great big bear. More terrified than

Suddenly the bear spoke to him and said, "It's all right. I won't hurt you. You can stay here and dry out."

"Stay here and I'll share some berries and fruit with you."

ever, he raced for the entrance of the cave, hoping to escape with his life. But suddenly the bear spoke to him and said, "It's all right. I won't hurt you. You can stay here and dry out. It is raining much too hard for you to find your way home tonight. Stay here and I'll share some berries and fruit and honey with you." The bear spoke so re-assuringly and gently that the man decided to stay in the dry cave despite his astonishment. He re-mained there for several days as the guest of the bear, enjoying the food and a warm, dry place to stay while the storm raged outside. Finally, one day the bear said, "It looks like the storm has subsided enough for you to be able to find your way home now." As the woodgatherer departed he thanked the bear profusely and said, "Is there any way I can ever repay your kindness?"

"Don't worry about it," said the bear, "The

only thing I ask is that you not mention to anyone
that there's a bear up here because a lot of people
like to hunt for bear meat."

"Of course," promised the woodgatherer, and
he was on his way.

On his way down the mountain, he met a hunter
who asked him, "Have you seen any wild beasts up
this way?"

"Yes," said the woodgatherer, "I saw a bear."

"Oh?" said the hunter, very interested.

"Yes, but he saved my life, so I don't want
to tell you where he is."

"Look," said the hunter, "a bear's a bear and
just a beast, after all. You and I are human and
need good meat in order to stay healthy and survive.
You can tell me where he is. After all, he's just
an animal. I'll share the meat with you and even
give you some of the hide to make a nice warm coat."
Enticing him like this, the hunter eventually per-
suaded the woodgatherer to lead him to the cave
where the big bear lived. The hunter shot the
bear, skinned it, gutted it, and began to slice
off big hunks of raw flesh. He started to hand
one of these big pieces of the bear's meat to the
woodgatherer, who reached out greedily to take it.
But just as he was about to grab the meat, both his
hands fell off. "What???" exclaimed the hunter.
"What kind of bad karma do you have that such a
thing should happen to you?"

"It's right," said the woodgatherer in fear
and dismay. "It's really what should happen to me.
That big bear treated me like my own father would

treat me and I let you shoot him. I really don't know how to repay kindness at all! This is just the retribution I deserve," he said, looking at his handless stumps. Witnessing this, the hunter dared not touch the meat either, so he took it down to the closest temple and said it should be distributed as offerings. But there was an Arhat at the temple and when he saw the meat he said, "No one can touch this meat. It cannot be eaten, for it is the flesh of a Bodhisattva. That bear was a Bodhisattva." He carefully carried the meat to a stupa, placed it on the altar, and after that, everyone made offerings and worshipped it.

* * *

CORPSE BODY

One day Revata went walking and lost his way. In the woods he happened upon an abandoned hut and decided to spend the night there. Once inside, however, he was joined by one of the biggest ghosts he'd ever seen, who was lugging a human corpse after him. Revata was terrified and didn't dare make a move. Shortly thereafter, another ghost, even taller and more hulking than the first, came storming in and started fighting with the first ghost over the corpse. Their heated argument was over who should get the corpse, the first ghost claiming it to be his and the second ghost fighting for possession.

After the two ghosts finished their prank, they went on their way still bickering and bullying one another.

Eventually, in the midst of this turmoil, they spied Revata and decided to let him judge who the owner of the corpse was. Frightened that they would make him the second corpse, Revata decided the only thing to do was tell the truth as he saw it, so he said, in a pretty shaky voice, "The corpse must belong to the first ghost; he came in with it."

Well, that did it! The second ghost was beside himself with rage and grabbed one of Revata's arms and pulled it right out of the socket. The first ghost, glad to have been decided the owner of the corpse, said to Revata, "Never mind, here," and he shoved the corpse's arm into Revata's shoulder. It stuck there. Meanwhile, the second ghost was tearing at Revata's other arm and finally got it loose. The first ghost quickly took the corpse's other arm and fitted it in Revata's other shoulder socket. Then the second ghost grabbed Revata's head and twisted it off and the first ghost replaced it with the corpse's head. This went on until his torso, legs, and everything else had been ripped off him and replaced with the corpse's body parts. After the two ghosts finished their prank they went on their way still bickering and bullying one another.

Revata came to from his ordeal wondering, "Am I me? Who am I now? Is this body mine?" He went on his way, worried as could be as to who could answer his burning question. Eventually he passed a Buddhist temple and knew that inside there must be Bhikshus who would know who he was. So he went in and blurted out to the first Bhikshus he saw, "Who am I? Am I me?"

"What in the world are you talking about?" they asked. "What makes you ask a question like that?" Then Revata told them about what had happened to him the night before.

The Bhikshus replied, "Not only are you not you now, you were never you. Originally your body was only a combination of the four elements--earth, fire, air and water." When Revata heard that, he enlightened to the meaning and asked to leave the home life.

YOU TOOK MY COW!

After having left the home life under the Buddha, Revata went up into the mountains to meditate. He worked hard at his cultivation and soon could sit still and enter samadhi. Before long he certified to Arhatship. Eventually a lot of people heard about his skill and came to study under him. He had five hundred disciples, all of whom also worked very hard to perfect the method Revata taught them. Soon they too became enlightened and were Arhats. After they accomplished Arhatship, they went back down the mountain to teach other people the method of cultivation they had learned, leaving Revata on the mountain alone to meditate. He sat in samadhi for long periods of time. Once, he looked down at his robe and saw that it was so old it had bleached in the sun and was almost white. He decided he should re-dye his robe the brownish-grey color that Bhikshus wear. So he found some tree bark and plant roots that would make the right color and set them to boiling in a pot over the fire. When the water was hot and had turned the right brownish color, he placed his robe in it. But the more he stirred, the more the robe became like leather--like the hide of a cow. And the more he stirred, the more the liquid turned reddish in color until it looked all too much like blood. Then he noticed that the bark and roots were turning into the flesh and bones of a cow and the whole pot was giving off the odor of beef stew. Clamping the lid on, he sat down beside the pot in samadhi and said, "My karmic retribution is coming! My karmic retribution is coming!"

Although he was usually quite alone there on the mountain, a cowherder suddenly appeared, striding toward him as if he were really angry. He immediately began cursing Revata, saying, "You no-good Bhikshu, what have you got in that pot? I can smell beef stew a mile away. You've blatantly broken the precept against killing and slaughtered my cow when it came along, and now you're cooking it up for your meal." With that, he pushed aside the lid of the pot and saw the red, bloody liquid, and the pieces of meat and bone, and the cowhide floating on top. "See! I caught you red-handed!" Grabbing the pot, he went down the mountain and into the village to take his complaint to the local ruler. Revata was called in and asked, "What do you have to say for yourself?"

"There's nothing I can say," was Revata's reply. So he was sentenced to twelve years in jail. As an inmate, however, he was very tidy, always sweeping out the cells and halls and being pleasant to all the prisoners. He was kind to all the unhappy people there and his kindness rubbed off. Pretty soon they started to be kind to one another as well.

Meanwhile, time passed, and when the twelve-year sentence was almost up, Revata's five hundred Arhat-disciples, who had been busy at their teaching, thought of their teacher and they all decided to pay him a visit to see how he was. Contemplating with their heavenly eyes they saw that he

When the king was told he had five hundred visitors on the roof-- all Arhats--he began to search his mind.

had been wrongly put in jail for twelve years.
Astounded and upset, they decided to go directly
to the King of that area to find out how such a
thing could have happened. Since they were Arhats,
they had spiritual penetrations. Instead of entering the palace the usual way, they flew up onto
the roof of the palace to show how insistent they
were on resolving the matter of their teacher's
imprisonment.

When the King was told he had five hundred
visitors on the roof--all Arhats--he began to
search his mind. They questioned him and he realized that he must have made a horrible mistake,
convicting the teacher of these Arhats and sentenc-
ing him to twelve years in prison. At this point,
the King went immediately to the jail and summoned
Revata, intending to repent of his misjudgment.
Expecting to be confronted by an outraged prisoner
displaying righteous indignation for having been
unjustly sentenced, the King was indeed surprised
when Revata appeared, in samadhi, calm and happy,
as if the twelve years he'd just spent in jail had
not caused him any problem. And in fact, the whole
jail had been transformed under Revata's compassionate influence. The prisoners were not afflicted but content and happy and the atmosphere was
more like a pleasure-garden than a jail.

When the King tried to apologize and beg for-
giveness, Revata passed it off, saying, "It was my
retribution. It was fitting for me to undergo it."

Later his five hundred disciples asked him
what he had meant and Revata related the following:

"I remember that in a past life, long, long ago, I was a cowherder and lost my cow one day in the mountains. I came upon a Pratyekabuddha sitting in meditation and wrongly accused him of stealing my cow. Not only that, but I dragged him down the mountain to the local law officers and detained him for twelve hours while I fought to prove my point. Since I detained a Pratyekabuddha in that way for twelve hours, it was my retribution in this life to have to be detained for twelve years to pay back that debt."

"I remember that in a past life, long, long ago, I was a cowherder and lost my cow one day in the mountains."

THE GREAT WHITE ELEPHANT

One day Subhuti asked the Buddha why Bodhisattvas sometimes take on the bodies of animals. The Buddha replied, "Bodhisattvas' hearts are very vast and they want to save all living beings. They manifest in all kinds of ways in order to do that.

"Bodhisattvas are different from Arhats and Pratyekabuddhas," the Buddha continued. "If Arhats and Pratyeka Buddhas are confronted by an enemy they will not fight back and they will not harbor resentment. But they have not reached the point where they can have kind thoughts towards their enemies. They have only gotten to the stage where they will refrain from treating an enemy like an enemy, but they cannot treat an enemy as they would their own son. A story will show you what I mean about Bodhisattvas.

"At one time there was a great Bodhisattva in the world, a mighty white elephant with six spectacular tusks. Because that elephant was so magnificent, many people wanted it. One day as the Bodhisattva was walking along, a hunter boldly put an arrow in his bow, aimed, and shot the elephant right in the heart. The great white elephant immediately knew that as a result of his action, the hunter would be killed by the surrounding herd of elephants over whom the white elephant reigned as king. His herd would certainly seek immediate revenge. Instantly, the great white elephant reached out and wrapped his trunk protectively around the hunter who had just shot him in the heart. Then the white elephant communicated with his mate who was assembling the herd to attack the hunter, 'You are the mate of a Bodhisattva,' he told his wife, 'How can you give rise to anger? The only reason he shot me is because he is troubled and afflicted about something.' Then, turning to the hunter he asked, 'Why did you shoot me?'

'Because I want your tusks,' was the greedy hunter's reply.

'Now do you understand?' the elephant said, admonishing his wife to leave off her attack. Then he took his trunk and pulled his long tusks out, giving them to the hunter. 'Go on your way. You have what you want and you are free to leave unharmed.'

"That is the way a Bodhisattva treats his enemies," concluded the Buddha. "That elephant Bodhisattva taught all the elephants in his herd a lesson in compassion."

* * *

THE SORRY SNAKE

Once long ago, there lived a man who was very industrious. Basically he wasn't rich, but he worked very hard and earned money because he had an obsession. He loved gold. He would toil at various jobs and bring home coins, but he was loathe to spend them. Instead, he would save up until he had enough coins to exchange for a gold piece. This went on for years and years until eventually he had seven pots full of gold. He hoarded every penny so he could exchange his common coins for gold ones. He thought of all kinds of

ways to get by so he wouldn't have to spend a cent.
He had his own garden which provided him with food.
He mended and remended his clothing in order to save
money.

When he wasn't working, he would sit in the
room next to his pots of gold and look at them.
He was always afraid someone would steal them. This
got to be such a fear that even when his friends
came to visit, he was convinced they were just waiting for an opportunity to rob him. So he scolded
them and drove them away, losing his temper all the
time out of concern for his gold. This constant
anxiety and violent temper took its toll and soon
he fell ill. But he couldn't part with any of the
money to pay a doctor, so he wasted away and died.

After his death, he was reborn as a snake which
found its way into the room where the gold was
stashed and guarded it so fiercely that no one
dared enter. The room remained empty except for
the pots of gold and the snake. When that snake
died, it took rebirth as a snake again and came
back to take up watch over the gold. This went
on for over ten thousand years. Life after life
the former snake took rebirth as a snake and it
seemed the process would never end.

Eventually a snake was born which had a bit
of sense. He realized that watching the seven pots
of gold was very dull business. "I don't want to
have to be reborn as a snake again," it decided.
"I'd like to do something else besides guard this
money. It's meaningless. But how can I get out
of this vicious cycle?" it wondered. With what
wits it had, it decided that if it could do some-

"I don't want to have to be reborn as a snake again,"
it decided. "I'd like to do something else besides
guard this money. It's meaningless."

thing good--for example, by helping people--then
maybe it would gain enough merit to insure it a
better rebirth. But how to go about it? Obviously,
the first step was to get out of that room. So it
slithered down to the roadside and hid in some tall
grass. There, it watched the passers-by until it
saw a man who appeared to be of strong character.
His features were full and he seemed kind and trust-
worthy. The snake slid out onto the road as he
passed and of course the man jumped away in fright.

"I want to do something good," said the snake.

"Don't go away. Don't be afraid," said the snake. "I don't want to harm you. I just want to ask a favor."

"But I know that snakes are very poisonous and I don't want to get close to you," said the man.

"I really don't want to hurt you," said the snake, "I just need some help." The man, who was gentle to begin with, relented and came near to listen to the snake's tale. "...and so I want to do something good," concluded the snake and indicated a Buddhist temple which lay in sight across the road. "I'd like to have you arrange for a meal offering at that temple and then come and get some of the gold to pay for it. On the day selected for the offering, I want you to take me into the temple with you so that I can bow to the Buddhas and take part in the services. That way I can amass some merit."

"All right," agreed the kind man and he went immediately to see if he could make such arrangements. Finding a person in charge of such things, he related his strange encounter with the snake and stated the snake's request. The monk agreed and a date was set seven days hence.

On the appointed day, the man came for the gold and the snake and gently covered the snake with a cloth so that the sun would not burn its tender skin as they walked the open road to the temple. On their way, a person stopped and asked where the man was headed and what he was going to do. He asked three times, but the man carrying

On their way, a person stopped and asked where the man was headed and what he was going to do.

the snake said nothing in reply. With each silence,
the snake, a beast with a violent nature to begin
with, was aroused to fierce anger. By the third
time, the snake was ready to kill the man carrying
him. With all its strength, the snake quelled the
impulse, realizing that this man was its benefactor
and that it should not harm him, much less kill
him. It took a great effort to keep from giving
in to its hateful urge, however, and after the man
had walked on a ways the snake said to him, "Better
put me down a minute." The man obliged and the
snake began to shout and scold him frantically.
"How could you be so arrogant and haughty? All
the man did was ask you a simple question and you
totally snubbed him. You're outrageous..." and so
it went, on and on, berating the man. Quickly
agreeing with the snake, the man acknowledged his
wrongdoing and promised never to be that way again.
Then the snake was able to go on, having vented
its anger.

Reaching the temple, they went inside and
were confronted with the exquisite images, the
tranquil atmosphere and the awesome virtue of the
assembled Sangha. After the meal offering was completed and the Abbot and monks began to file into
the dining hall, the snake lay transfixed as they
passed it by. Looking up at the monks, the snake
perceived their purity and compassion, their awe-
someness and strength and thought that it had never
seen such a beautiful sight before. Its heart was
filled with joy at the opportunity to make offerings to them and join in worship. After the meal
the Abbot spoke Dharma which delighted the snake.

It was so moved that it told the monk in charge, "I have six more pots of gold that I will bring here so that it can be used to do the Buddha's work."

After the snake died, it was reborn in the Heaven of the Thirty-Three and when that blissful reward was ended, it was reborn as a man at the time of Shakyamuni Buddha. Encountering the Dharma, the man had the opportunity to leave home and he became first in wisdom among the Buddha's disciples. He was Shariputra.

THE TORTOISE KING

Once there was a gigantic tortoise who was in fact a Bodhisattva come in the body of a tortoise in order to teach and transform aquatic creatures. He lived in the ocean and instructed the shrimp, turtles, fish, and oysters to hold the precepts and cultivate the Way, and everyone got along very well together.

One day the tortoise walked out onto the sandy shore, and there in the warm sun he got sleepy. He lay down to take a nap, but because he was such a big tortoise, the "nap" turned out to last for months and months. Shortly after he fell asleep, a group of merchants came along and set up a shop on his back. Since the tortoise was so huge, they could not detect it was his back. To them, it seemed like a piece of solid land in the midst of shifting sands. They constructed stores and homes, trafficked back and forth in their carts and carriages, grazed their animals and built their fires, right there on the King Tortoise's back. Eventually this business woke the tortoise up, especially the heat from their fires. He found that he was extremely uncomfortable. Their buildings were heavy and their fires were hot. He wanted to get up and go cool himself off in the surf. But being a Bodhisattva, he didn't want to hurt them, and he knew that if he moved they might be harmed and would certainly be scared. So he lay still and was patient with the suffering. Eventually he could take no more and rose to try to cool off by walking a bit. Immediately, the colony on his back began to panic.   "Earthquake!" they exclaimed, running hither and thither. The tortoise ambled slowly but deliberately down to the water's edge, thinking that if he just submerged his underside in the cool water it might ease his agony. When the inhabitants on his shell saw the water rising all around them, they were terrified. "Flood!" they screamed, "We'll all be drowned!" Hearing their desperation, the tortoise spoke to them saying, "Don't be afraid. I won't hurt you. You won't be knocked off and you won't drown. You see, I'm a tortoise and you've taken up housing on my shell. I'll set you safely down, though, never fear."

The tortoise then turned and brought his burden back to safe, dry ground where the whole group of merchants climbed down off his shell. They were so moved that they all bowed to the big tortoise and made this vow: "You are truly a Bodhisattva! You saved our lives. In the future when you become a Buddha, please cross us over."

And in the future, the tortoise did become a Buddha--Shakyamuni Buddha, in fact--and the five hundred merchants who had lived on his back became Shariputra and his five hundred disciples who all certified to the fruit and crossed over the sea of birth and death.

THE GARDEN OF THE BENEFACTOR
OF ORPHANS AND THE SOLITARY

I. WINNING IT

In Shravasti lived the Elder Sudatta, who believed in the Buddhadharma. Since there was no one else in Shravasti who believed as he did, he decided to ask the Buddha to come there and speak Dharma, to teach and transform the people of that city. Upon making the request, he was told by the Buddha that there would have to be a place for all his disciples to stay--a pure and quiet place where the Dharma could be spoken. Sudatta asked if he might donate such a place, and Shakyamuni Buddha gave silent consent. Plans began to be formulated, and the Buddha decided to send Shariputra along with the Elder Sudatta, because Shariputra was wise, replete with spiritual penetrations, and had an awesome manner. The Elder Sudatta then asked Shariputra how far the Buddha could travel in a day if he did not make use of his Penetration of the Complete Spirit. The answer was that he could travel about twenty miles a day--the distance a Wheel-Turning King is capable of travelling. So as Shariputra and Sudatta made their way to Shravasti, they arranged that every twenty miles a comfortable resting place would be established, so that in the future when the Buddha made the journey to Shravasti, he would be accommodated as he came.

Once in the city, Shariputra and Sudatta began to search for just the right location, but found nothing until they happened upon Prince Jeta's

Grove, which was just right. The negotiations
they had to go through with the Prince to acquire
the Garden are another whole story. After they
succeeded in purchasing the Garden, the six masters
of outside ways who resided in the City got wind
of the plan to establish a Way-place there and
they immediately went to the King. "We won't have
it," they said. "The only way Shakyamuni and his
followers can come here is if they can defeat us
in a public contest. We'll match wits and see who
wins. If we win, then Shakyamuni can't come. If
they win, then that's another matter." The emperor
called Sudatta in to inform him of this turn of
events. Sudatta took the news very hard and was
sunk in depression for days afterwards. When he
next encountered Shariputra he was dishevelled,
with unkempt clothes and hair, and deep concern
and worry written in the lines of his face.

"What's happened to you!" Shariputra exclaimed.
"What's brought you to this?"

Sudatta said, "I don't think we're going to
be able to make the Garden into a Way place after
all." And then he told Shariputra about his sum-
mons before the King.

"A contest, you say? Is that what's bother-
ing you?" said Shariputra, "Well, worry no more.
I can handle all of those masters and their disciples put together. Even all of them in Jambu-
dvipa put together cannot move a single hair on my
foot. The more the merrier. It's okay, bring
them on!"

With that, Sudatta cheered up considerably.

He took a bath, put on clean clothes and went before the King. "All right," he said, "We accept the challenge." The date of the contest was arranged for seven days hence.

On that day, the drum was hit. There were three types of drums. The first was a copper drum that would call twelve million people together. The next was a silver drum that would call fourteen million people together. The third and largest was a golden drum which would summon everyone in the whole land together. For this contest, the golden drum was beaten and people began to stream in from far and wide. A platform was erected for the six masters, who were surrounded by their three hundred billion disciples. Opposite was another platform containing one seat for Shariputra, who was accompanied only by Sudatta. People had arrived and the hour was at hand. Meanwhile, Shariputra had sat down quietly under a tree and entered samadhi. He contemplated the multitude assembling and thought, "These six masters and their disciples are very arrogant. What virtuous conduct would move these people to feel respect?" Then he thought, "If in the past I have been filial to my father and mother throughout uncountable kalpas, and if I have been respectful of the Sangha during all that time, then people should automatically respect me."

Meanwhile, no one noticed Shariputra under a tree and the six masters decided that he had simply failed to show up for the contest. They marched off to see the King and said, "Shakyamuni's disciple hasn't even dared show his face. Who can blame him? He must realize he can never be a match for the power we've got assembled here."

The King summoned Sudatta and said, "Where's your teacher's disciple? Go get him. It's time to begin the contest."

Sudatta went to where Shariputra was sitting, knelt before him with his palms together, and said quietly, "Venerable One, the multitude has arrived. It's time to begin." Shariputra slowly came out of samadhi, stood up and began to walk through the throng. His pace was so majestic, his bearing so awesome, that he was like a lion as he moved through the crowd. Without realizing what they were doing, the entire assembly stood as he passed and with one accord bowed to him most respectfully. His deportment called forth this response in their hearts.

Among the disciples of the six masters was one named Lao Du Ch'a who was especially skilled in the use of spiritual penetrations. At that point he transformed himself into a gigantic tree which spread out its branches to shade the entire assembly. Abundant with foliage and laden with fruit, the tree was a magnificent sight. The crowd all gasped and said, "Oh, Lao Du Ch'a has transformed himself!" Then Shariputra turned into a violent wind which blew the tree down by its roots and then blew it all to bits. The crowd roared, "Shariputra wins!"

Then Lao Du Ch'a turned into a pool surrounded by the seven jewels and adorned with lotus flowers. It was an exquisite sight and the crowd all gasped,

Then Lao Du Ch'a appeared as a ten-headed dragon, but Shariputra transformed into a Great Golden-Winged P'eng Bird and slurped the dragon down in one gulp.

"Lao Du Ch'a has transformed himself!" Then Shariputra transformed into a great white elephant replete with six tusks. On the end of each tusk were seven lotus flowers and atop each lotus flower were seven jade-like maidens. The splendid creature ambled slowly and majestically over to the pool and proceeded to drink it dry. The crowd roared, "Shariputra wins!"

Then Lao Du Ch'a transformed into a tall mountain formed of the seven gems. On its sides welled forth bubbling springs and the forests were rich with flowers and fruits. The crowd sighed, "Lao Du Ch'a has transformed himself!" Then Shariputra changed into a Vajra-Power Knight wielding a Vajra Pestle. He proceeded to smash the mountain to smithereens. The crowd roared, "Shariputra wins!"

Then Lao Du Ch'a appeared as a ten-headed dragon which rained down gems in space and brought forth terrifying lightning and thunder as well as earthquakes. The crowd shuddered, "Lao Du Ch'a has transformed himself!" Then Shariputra turned into a Great Golden Winged P'eng Bird and slurped the dragon down in one gulp. The crowd roared, "Shariputra wins again!"

Then Lao Du Ch'a turned into a mighty ox with thick muscular legs and sharp vicious horns. It pawed the ground, lowered its mighty head, and charged. The crowd drew back shouting, "Lao Du Ch'a has transformed himself!" Then Shariputra turned into a gigantic lion and ate the ox all up. The crowd roared, "Shariputra wins!"

Then Lao Du Ch'a turned into a ferocious

Then Shariputra turned into a gigantic lion and ate the ox all up. The crowd roared, "Shariputra wins!"

yaksha ghost. Its body was gigantic and massive.
Fire poured out of its head. Its eyes were like
pools of blood, and it spit fire continually from
its mouth. It stomped and stormed around, terrifying absolutely everyone in the assembly. "Lao
Du Ch'a has transformed himself!" they screamed.
Then Shariputra turned into King Vaishravana and
it was the yaksha's turn to be terrified, so
threatening was the King's appearance. The yaksha sought to retreat and run but fire suddenly
broke out all around except on the side where Shariputra stood. Lao Du Ch'a threw himself down and
admitted defeat, begging for mercy. As soon as he
surrendered all the fires went out of their own
accord. "Shariputra's won!" the crowd roared.
"Lao Du Ch'a is defeated!"

Then Shariputra ascended into space and manifested spiritual transformations. He displayed
the four awesome deportments of walking, standing,
sitting, and lying down right in emptiness. He
emitted fire from the lower part of his body and
water from the upper part. He emitted water
from the lower part and fire from the upper part.
He disappeared in the east and reappeared in the
west. He disappeared in the west and reappeared
in the east. He disappeared in the north and reappeared in the south. He disappeared in the south
and reappeared in the north. He manifested a big
body and then a small body. He manifested one body
that turned into many millions of bodies, and then
back into one body. He walked in space as if it
were earth. He entered the earth as if it were
water. He walked on water as if it were

-33-

earth. After manifesting these eighteen transformations of an Arhat he hid away his Penetration of the Complete Spirit and sat down in the midst of the assembly. Seeing Shariputra manifest the spiritual powers gladdened the hearts of all in the assembly. Then Shariputra spoke Dharma for them and their bliss grew even greater. All obtained certification to the various levels of Arhatship, each according to his or her past causes and conditions. The three hundred billion disciples of the six masters left the home life under Shariputra.

Shariputra and Sudatta went back to the Garden of the Benefactor of Orphans and the Solitary to measure off the land in preparation for erecting the Way-place. As they were each holding an end of the string to measure off the lengths, Shariputra smiled. Sudatta asked, "Venerable One, why do you smile?" Shariputra replied, "Because of the merit and virtue you have established from donating this garden, you already have your choice of heavenly palaces awaiting you." Then by means of Shariputra's spiritual penetrations, Sudatta was able to see up through the six desire heavens. He asked Shariputra, "Which is the best place to go?" Shariputra replied, "Those in the first three heavens still experience desire, so it would be better not to get reborn there. The two uppermost heavens don't involve themselves in worldly matters at all but as a result the beings are haughty and think they are very special. The best heaven of the desire realm is the fourth one, the Tushita. It's the place where the Bodhisattvas who will be the next Buddha go, and so while in that heaven one can draw near them and hear the Buddhadharma.

Then Shariputra suddenly looked sad and Sudatta asked, "Venerable One, what troubles you?" Shariputra replied, "Do you see the ants on the ground here?!"

"Yes," Sudatta replied.

"In the past at the time of Vipashyin Buddha, you also used this place to establish a pure abode for that Buddha, and these ants you see here now were also ants then. At the time of Shikhin Buddha you also used this place to establish a pure abode for that Buddha, and these ants were ants then, too. You also used this land to establish a Way-Place for Vishvabhu Buddha, and the ants you see here now were ants at that time, too. You used this same ground to make a Bodhimanda for Krakucchanda Buddha, and the ants that had been ants from the time of Vipashyin Buddha continued to be ants. You also made this a place of Pure Dwelling for Kanakamuni Buddha, and the ants that were ants before continued to be ants at that time. You also used this place to establish a Bodhimanda for Kashyapa Buddha, and the ants were still undergoing rebirth as ants at that time. And now you have used this ground to set up a Way-Place for Shakyamuni Buddha, and still, the ants are the same ones being reincarnated again and again. My sadness comes from knowing how difficult it is to escape the cycle of rebirth as an animal. It's been ninety-one great kalpas (16,800,000 years equal one small kalpa; 336,000,000 years equal one middle-sized kalpa; 1,334,000,000 years equal one great kalpa) and still these ants that were ants then are ants now."

Elder Sudatta had a dwelling of Chandana wood constructed for the Buddha to use and also erected a massive building to house the twelve hundred fifty Bhikshus. There were one hundred and twenty places to hit the boards. When all was in readiness, Sudatta knew it was time to ask the Buddha to come to Shravasti. But he feared that if he went without informing the King, the King might be displeased. So he asked for an audience and it turned out that the King not only welcomed the Buddha, but insisted upon sending a royal greeting party to invite the Buddha and accompany him to Shravasti.

When the Buddha arrived, he emitted a great light that shone over everything in the three thousand great thousand worlds. As he tread the ground the earth trembled and shook. In the city, music spontaneously burst forth and the drums rolled by themselves. The blind could suddenly see, the deaf could hear, the mute could speak, and those who were hunchbacked stood erect. Cripples were made whole. When the multitude of men and women, young and old, saw these auspicious responses, they were so happy they jumped for joy and came to where the Buddha was. Eighteen million people gathered in the Garden. When they heard the Dharma their various causes and conditions led to various responses: some attained the first, second, third, or fourth fruit of Arhatship, some planted the seed for becoming Pratyekabuddhas, and some brought forth the mind for unsurpassed Bodhi.

Eventually the time came to pass when the

Elder Sudatta was about to die. The Buddha certified that he was a third stage Arhat by that time
and after his death he was indeed born in the
Tushita Heaven. How do we know? It is because
after he arrived at the Tushita Heaven, Sudatta
still could not part with the Buddha and wanted
to return to pay his respects one more time and
let him know where he was. So one day there was
a brilliant light in the Garden and Sudatta came
before the Buddha, saying, "I am Sudatta, also
named Anathapindaka."

UPSIDE-DOWN DRAGON

Once there was an Arhat who visited a certain dragon king in his palace in order to speak Dharma for him. The Arhat would take his bowl, go to the dragon's palace, accept an offering of food from the dragon, speak Dharma, and then return. When he got back, he would give his bowl to a young novice to wash. One day a few grains of rice were left in the bowl and the novice ate them. He was enchanted by the taste. "There's nothing like this food in the whole world!" he thought. "I'm going to follow my teacher next time and see if I can get a whole bowlful of it!" Next time his teacher set out in his bell (which in those days was wrapped with rope) the young novice clung to the ropes on the bottom of the bell and rode along to the dragon palace, relying on the spiritual powers of the Arhat. When the dragon saw that he had two visitors, he thought to himself: "Who's this other one? He doesn't have any spiritual penetrations. How did he get here? Well, I'll just have to make offerings to him, too."

Since the young novice didn't have any samadhi, he began looking around and was taken by the female dragons, the palace itself and the commanding air of the Dragon King. "I'd like to be a dragon myself," he decided.

Meanwhile, the Dragon King warned the Arhat not to bring the youngster back with him anymore. But when the novice got back to the temple, the memory of the dragon palace and the idea he'd conceived to become a dragon himself didn't leave him.

He cultivated hard but when he transferred the
merit of his work, instead of saying, "I vow to
be reborn in the Pure Land," he'd say, "I vow to
be reborn as a dragon." Eventually the idea took
total possession of him. While meditating, he saw
the large pool at the base of the temple and he
knew that his vow would be fulfilled. He rushed
out to the pool, threw his robe over his head, and
jumped in. He drowned and sure enough was reborn
as a great big dragon in that very pool.

Being bigger than the other dragon who inhabited the pool, he was able to kill it off in
their first tussle. From then on he reigned supreme
in the pool. But whenever the monks happened to
spy him they would admonish him and say, "How upside
down you are!" The Shami-turned-dragon ignored them,
however, and remained content with the lot he'd
chosen for himself.

LONG IS THE ROUND OF REBIRTH
TO THE FOOLISH

During the time of the Buddha there was a
king named Prasenajit. One day, when there was a
festival going on in the city, the King went out
into the streets to enjoy the activities. Of course
as he passed through the city he attracted a lot
of attention to himself because he was a king. At
one point, a woman opened the shuttered window of
her house and looked out to watch the King pass.
At the same time the King noticed her and was attracted by her beauty. After a moment she withdrew
and closed the window. But the King could not for-
get how lovely she was and gave rise to improper
thoughts about her. When he returned to the palace
he asked one of his officials if he had noticed the
woman looking out the window and if he hadn't found
her to be beautiful. The official had noticed her
and agreed that she was indeed lovely. The King
then told him to find out if the woman was married
or not. When the official later returned with word
that she was in fact married, the King said, "Fine.
Tell her husband I want to see him."

The husband was nervous at being called before
the King and yet was careful to arrive promptly for
the interview. The King informed him, "From now
on I want you to be my personal attendant. At all
times you are to be by my side ready to serve my
needs."

The man was a poor fellow and the thought of
acting as the King's attendant terrified him. Most
respectfully he suggested that he would be willing

to work and have his wages taxed so as to serve
the King in that way, rather than to be his personal attendant. But the King refused his offer
and said, "No, I want you right here with me."
Because he was utterly petrified of making a mistake, the man was always attentive to his job and
as time passed, the King could find no fault with
him. King Prasenajit was just waiting for the fellow to do something wrong so he could execute him,
but the man kept doing everything right.

Eventually the King grew impatient and decided
he would have to devise a plan whereby the man was
bound to go wrong. Then the King could do away
with him and take his wife for his own. So one
morning he said to his attendant, "Today I have an
errand for you to run. You are to go to such-and-
such a river and bring back a water-lily and some
red clay. However, you must be sure to be back
here with these things before it's time for my
afternoon bath." The King knew full well that a
water-lily and red clay could only be gotten from
the Dragon Palace. Surely this simple man would
have no way to obtain them. If he failed to bring
them back, then the King would have a legitimate
reason for punishing him.

Wrought with anxiety, the man rushed to his
home and burst in the door. "Pack me some lunch.
I have to run an errand for the King and be back
by his bath time today. Hurry!" His wife threw
food into a bag--some new and some old--and he was
off and running. As he hurried on his way he knew
he dared not stop to eat, so when hunger overtook

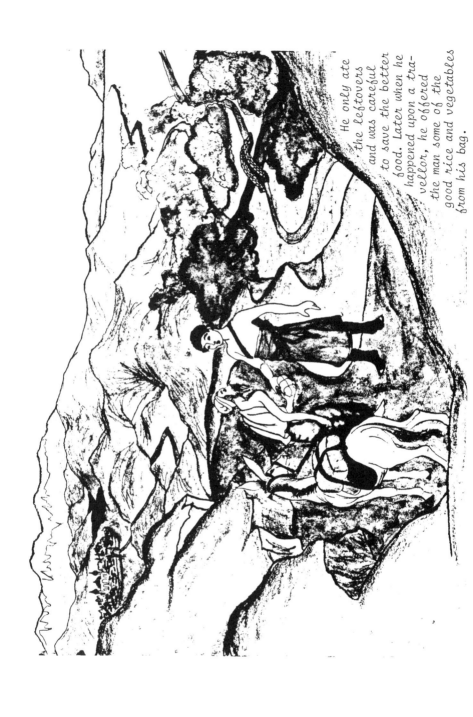

He only ate the leftovers and was careful to save the better food. Later when he happened upon a traveller, he offered the man some of the good rice and vegetables from his bag.

him, he dipped into the bag of food and ate as he
raced along the road. He only ate the leftovers
his wife had packed, however. He was careful to
leave untouched the better food. Later, when he
happened upon a traveller, he offered the man some
of the good rice and vegetables from his bag. The
traveller accepted the gift gratefully and ate the
food. Hurrying on, the man finally arrived at the
banks of the designated river. The first thing he
did was toss the remaining good rice over the surface of the river as he called out, "Come, fish,
and eat this food. It's my gift to you." Then he
called out in a louder voice, "Dragon King, today
on the road I gave a portion of my good food to a
traveller and thereby amassed some blessings. Just
now I gave another part of my lunch to the fish in
these waters and added some more blessings. I
would like to dedicate to you all those blessings
from my acts of giving and in return I ask that you
bring me a water lily and some red clay."

The Dragon King heard him well enough, but he
manifested on the banks of the river as an old man
and said, "What? Repeat yourself." The man repeated his offering and his request. The old fellow asked again, "What did you say?" and the King's
attendant stated his offer once more. Upon hearing
it three times the Dragon King knew that he must be
telling the truth. "So you're really willing to
give me those blessings that accrued to you today?"
he said. "All right I'll exchange them for the
things you need." And he gave the attendant a
water lily and some red clay.

Next came the long journey back to the palace. Working against time, the attendant ran as fast as his legs would carry him. Meanwhile the King was full of nasty thoughts. He was sure that the attendant would never be able to get the Dragon King to give over the items he named, but what if... Just to be doubly sure, he decided he'd take his bath earlier than usual and that he would lock up the main palace gates and keep the key with him in the bath chamber. Then, even if by some rare chance the attendant did get the things and did make it back to the palace on time, he still would not be able to present them to the King prior to his bath. He wouldn't be able to get in the palace and the King would already be bathing. That would ensure that the King could punish him by having him executed for failing to carry out orders.

And that's the way things went. The attendant arrived back at the palace on time and was extremely relieved, until he realized that the palace gates were locked tight. Pounding on them and shouting at the top of his voice, he aroused the gatekeeper. But it didn't do any good because the keeper didn't have the key. "The King himself took the key today. I have no way to let you in."

Desperate to finish his task, the attendant spread the red clay out on the door sill and hung the water lily above the door. Then he called out to those in the courtyards, "Please come and witness. Notice the time and see that I have returned with a water lily and red clay, just as I was instructed to do." But witnesses or no, the gate

At the stroke of midnight he heard four horrendous sounds.
"DU!" "SA!" "NA!" "SO!" What could they possibly mean?

remained locked and the dejected attendant stood outside knowing that his mission had failed. Finally, he turned and walked away, wondering where he would spend the night. Remembering that there was a Buddhist temple near the palace, he decided to go there. He said to himself, "The monks are kind and compassionate. They will certainly take me in for the night."

The King was busy in his chambers that evening making plans to execute the husband the following morning and then take the man's wife. He was having so much false thinking, in fact, that he could not go to sleep. He was still wide awake when at the stroke of midnight he heard four horrendous sounds. "DU! SA! NA! SO!" "What could they possibly mean?" he wondered, shuddering at their impact. "Is my throne going to be usurped? Does it mean I'm going to die?" If he was sleepless before, he was even more so now. One o'clock came and went. Three o'clock came and went. And finally it was morning but he'd not slept at all. As soon as he got up, he called for his astrologer to come for consultation as quickly as possible. When the court astrologer arrived, the King told him about the sounds in the night and repeated the syllables. "What do they mean?" he demanded.

Now to be perfectly truthful, the astrologer didn't have the slightest idea what they meant. But he was afraid to be dishonored. So he simply made something up. "Oh..." he said, "They're very, very inauspicious!"

"In what way," cried the King. "Be more specific!"

"Well..." said the astrologer, "They mean you are due to die."

"Isn't there anything that can be done?" asked the distraught King. "Isn't there some way to change my fate?"

"Yes," fibbed the astrologer, "you should gather one hundred elephants, one hundred horses, one hundred bulls, one hundred cows, one hundred sheep, one hundred chickens, and one hundred young men and one hundred young women and sacrifice them all. In this way we can turn the tides of fate."

Immediately the King issued an edict calling for one hundred of each kind of animal and human. But King Prasenajit basically had a really nasty temper and the entire kingdom was afraid of him, so instead of assembling one hundred of each, the people assembled five hundred of each, just for good measure. You can imagine all the braying and bleeting and mooing and weeping and wailing that ensued as the animals and people destined for sacrifice were brought into the courtyards. The ruckus didn't go undetected by Queen Mallika. She went into the King's chambers and asked, "What's happening today. Are you somehow indisposed?" The King related to her the events of his sleepless night and his astrologer's verdict on how to alleviate the impending disaster. When he finished, the Lady Mallika just stood staring at him. Finally she said, "You mean you intend to offer up all those beings in sacrifice? You're going to take all those lives just in order to save your own? For all your massive wealth, powerful position, and rank and status, you are certainly stupid! Let us go immediately and find the Buddha. He will have the wisdom to know how to best resolve this problem."

The King accompanied her and they went into the nearby temple where they found the Buddha, made obeisance, and then stood off to one side. King Prasenajit was so frightened about his impending doom that he could not speak. After a bit of silence, the Buddha gently encouraged him saying, "Oh great King, what brings you here today?" Still too scared and upset to express himself, the King remained speechless. Lady Mallika took the lead and explained to the Buddha about the four sounds that the King had heard in the night and the subsequent preparations for sacrifice.

When she finished, the Buddha comforted the King saying, "Don't worry, don't be frightened. Those sounds are not an indication that you are to die." And then the Buddha proceeded to tell this tale:

"At the time of Kashyapa Buddha there were four brothers. They were extremely wealthy men-- billionaires or trillionaires or some such. They had so much money they didn't know what to do with it, so they got together to try to decide how to spend it. The first one said, 'Kashyapa Buddha is in the world and he is doing good things for people. I think we should give our money to help support the Buddha's work. We could give to the poor and the homeless and aged.' But the other three couldn't agree. The second one thought they should spend their money on the best of wines, meat, and

good things to eat and buy elegant clothing and
fine houses. The third thought they should buy
carts and carriages and ships to carry them to see
the world. The fourth thought if they made presents
to beautiful women they could win their favors. He
was very convincing and eventually the brothers all
were turned by the fourth one's idea. So they spent
their time and money on beautiful women, women who
often were already married. Because of this bad
karma they created, when they died they fell into
the avici hell. There the suffering they endured
was uninterrupted and unspeakably horrible. When
the time came that they finally got out of that hell,
they were reborn to endure another hell--this time
the hell of boiling oil. In that hell there was
a vast pot filled to the brim with oil so hot it
was kept in a rolling boil. The four brothers'
torture was to slowly sink from the top of that oil
to the bottom of the pot and then to slowly rise
back up again, all the while being boiled by the
oil. Their descent took thirty thousand years and
their ascent to the surface took another thirty
thousand years. But that was only the first round.
When they reached the surface of the oil, all four
of their heads bobbed up simultaneously for a moment and they each called out as if to speak to one
another. But since they were immediately to begin
their second descent, they each got out only the
first sound of the first word of their sentences
before they once again became submerged in the oil.
One brother called out "Du!" another "Sa!" another
"Na!" and the last "So!" before their voices were

cut off. What do you suppose they were about to say to one another?" the Buddha asked his listeners.

"The first brother was about to say, '<u>Do</u> you realize that everything we did in our entire lives was evil? When you have wealth and you don't use it to give in order to benefit others but instead you spend it as we did, the wealth turns against you and becomes the source of disasters.'

"The second brother was about to say, '<u>Say</u>, this is very difficult to bear. We've been under for sixty thousand years, and who knows when we'll ever get out of here!'

"'<u>Now</u> when I think of how you and I used to laugh and joke when we were rich and how we played around, it makes this bitter retribution even more difficult to endure,' was what the third one wanted to say.

"And the fourth was about to announce, '<u>Soon</u> as I get a human body again I'm going to do nothing but good. I'm going to cultivate and hold the precepts and practice giving in a big way!'"

Of course, when King Prasenajit heard the story he immediately thought of his own plan to do away with the husband and take the beautiful wife-- exactly the kind of karma the four brothers had created that sent them to that pot of boiling oil. The King thought, "Well, I'm sure glad I didn't go through with that. From now on I won't be so greedy for beauty--especially when it belongs to someone else. Aloud he said to the Buddha, "World Honored One, last night was the longest night of my life."

Long is the round of rebirth to the foolish who do not know the True Law.

You remember that the husband had spent the night at the temple and so he came to be in the assembly when the King and Queen came to consult with the Buddha. He now spoke up and said, "World Honored One, yesterday I walked the longest road I've ever walked."

The Buddha smiled gently, acknowledging both their comments and then spoke this verse:

> Long is the night to him who is awake.
> Long is the mile to him who is tired.
> Long is the round of rebirth to
>   the foolish
> Who do not know the True Law.

Having learned his lesson, the King returned to the palace and immediately ordered that all the beings destined for sacrifice be released. The joy they expressed was uproarious and the five hundred young men and five hundred young women all shouted, "Queen Mallika has saved us! Queen Mallika has saved us!" for it was she who relied on the Buddha's wisdom to resolve the problem.

The verse the Buddha recited to sum up the event became part of the DHAMMAPADA and was often recited by the monks. It happened that a wealthy Brahman would hear the verse being recited when he passed by the temple, and the last two lines stuck in his mind. "Long is the round of rebirth to the foolish who do not know the True Law." He couldn't figure out what it really meant. He was well-to-do, influential in the city and was a handsome man with a beautiful wife. All the finer things of life were readily available to him, and yet he kept

coming back to that verse in his mind. Finally
one day he stopped and went into the temple to try
to find out more about the meaning of the verse.
There he saw the Buddha surrounded by the monks and
he respectfully made obeisance. Then he asked,
"Buddha, how many Buddhas will appear in the world
in the future?"

"Their number will be like sands in the Ganges
River," was the Buddha's reply. Hearing that there
would be that many more Buddhas to come made the
Brahman very happy. He expressed his delight and
said, "How wonderful! I will have an opportunity
to share my wealth and do the Buddha's work again
and again!"

Happy in heart, he bowed and took his leave.
But once on the road again he thought, "Oh! I
only asked the Buddha how many Buddhas there would
be in the future. I forgot to ask how many Buddhas
there have already been in the past." So he went
right back, bowed and asked that question of the
Buddha.

"Their number is also like sands in the Ganges
River," was the Buddha's reply. Hearing that, the
Brahman became very sad. "How could it be that I
have missed so many opportunities to gain true understanding? After the appearance of all those
Buddhas I'm still undergoing birth and death? I
certainly don't want to have to go through all the
future Buddhas to the number of sands in the Ganges
before I finally come to an awakening! And it's
not for sure that I'll even get to be reborn
as a person again for a long time. I'd better

really take advantage of the opportunity I have now in this life having met this one Buddha." With that, he resolved to leave home. After becoming a monk he was diligent in his practice and eventually certified to Arhatship. It's said that it's not easy to leave home and practice the Way when one is rich, but this Brahman was able to do so.

ARE YOU A HUMAN BEING?

It's not easy to gain rebirth as a human being. But one must be a human being in order to
leave the home life. Once there was a dragon who
really admired left home people and decided that
the grandest thing would be if he could leave home.
Being a dragon, he had spiritual powers and could
transform himself into a human being temporarily,
although he remained a dragon. So he transformed
himself and came to the Jeta Grove to ask if he
could leave the home life. The Buddha's disciples
did not realize that he was a dragon who had changed
into a human being and so they shaved his head.
Now dragons really like to sleep and this dragon
was no exception. At the monastery he shared a
living space with another monk. One day when his
roommate had gone out to beg for food the dragon/
monk thought, "Ah, now's my chance for a snooze."
He stretched out on his bed, but as soon as he fell
asleep, he could no longer keep himself in human
form. So he turned back into a big old dragon
stretched across the sleeping mat. When his roommate returned he opened the door and then slammed
it shut and started yelling, "Snake! snake! snake!"
alarming the whole monastery. When the monks came
running and opened the door, there was nothing inside but the monk, lying on his sleeping mat.
"What's going on?" they demanded of the frightened
roommate. "But really," he exclaimed, "there was
a huge snake or something in that room when I came
back just now."

The monks all went before the Buddha and the dragon/monk admitted that in fact he was a dragon who changed into a human being so that he could leave the home life. So the Buddha made a rule that from then on, whenever someone wants to leave home, when they are about to take the precepts, they must be asked the question, "Are you a human being?" And to this day, that question is always asked.

Even so, another one slipped by. An asura also had a sincere admiration for left home people and he, too, wanted to become a monk. Being part of the eightfold division, he, too, had spiritual powers and turned himself in the likeness of a person. The monks failed to recognize his true nature and allowed him to leave home. Things went along all right until the time when five hundred monks were invited to receive offerings. Being pushy and competitive, the asura managed to get first in line. When they arrived at the food, he crammed in all the rice destined for the five hundred monks. By the time he was finished, the meal period was over and all the other monks moved up in line only to find there was nothing to eat. The cooks were amazed, for they had prepared more than enough for five hundred hungry monks. Finally the finger was pointed at the asura. "He ate it all and he says he's not full yet!"

The monks took the asura/monk before the Buddha. When he was questioned he admitted that in fact he was not a human being but was an asura in disguise. And so he provided another reason for people being asked, "Are you a human being?" before they are allowed to leave home.

HE FORGOT EVERYTHING

Once three Shastra Masters made a pact that
they would all vow to be reborn in the inner court
of the Tushita Heaven when they died. There, they
would be able to listen to the Dharma spoken by
Maitreya Bodhisattva and they thought that would be
fine indeed. As a part of their pact they agreed
that whoever went first would return to tell the
others what it was like. Some time after, one of
the Shastra Masters died. But time passed and he
didn't return to tell the others anything at all.
They were both put out and wondered whatever could
have happened to him that he forgot to keep his
promise.

Later on another of the Shastra Masters died.
The one remaining Master waited and waited but it
was a whole year before the Master who was second
to die returned to let his friend know what was
happening. "Where have you been? What have you
been doing all this time? It's been such a long
time since you died and this is the first word I've
had from you."

"No," denied the second master. "I got to the
inner court of the Tushita Heaven and listened to
one short Dharma talk by Maitreya Bodhisattva. Then
I came right here to let you know how it was. It's
not been any time at all!" But of course he had
forgotten to reckon that time in the heavens goes
by much faster than time on earth. So what seemed
to him a short time in the heavens had actually
been a whole year in worldly time.

"What about our friend, the first to die?

What's going on that I haven't heard anything from him?" asked the living Shastra Master.

"Oh, him" said the second master, "He got born in the Tushita Heaven all right, but he made the mistake of getting born in the outer court instead of the inner one. It's a shame, a real disgrace. He's forgotten everything! All he does all day is enjoy the pleasures of the heavens--fine food, beautiful women, heavenly music, travelling palaces, exquisite garments, and so forth. Let me tell you, vowing to get reborn in the heavens is dangerous business!"

WALKING-STICK SIU

The sun was just rising over the mountain, when Mrs. Liang and Siu and all the other village mothers and daughters picked up their laundry baskets and walked to the river.

Soon the quiet river was full of talking mothers washing clothes in the water up and down the river. A few older girls helped with the washing, carrying bundles out to their mothers in the deeper water and taking the washed clothes back to the river bank, while the younger ones played together on the river's edge or waded in a shallow spot.

Only Walking-stick Siu sat alone. She could not run and play with the others. Her mother said she was no help at all. Now and then other mothers would look at Siu as she limped past with her walking stick in hand. Siu was a strange child, they thought. What good could she be? She would never be any help at all.

Usually, the mothers laughed and talked when they did the laundry. But today, the mothers did not laugh. The sickness had come. Many old people were sick, and now even some of the children were sick. Siu's younger brother was among those sick.

The mothers were worried. No one knew how long the sickness would last. No one knew when they would get better. It was a hard time. All the men were away now building the Emperor's new road. Alone, the mothers were afraid of the sickness.

Walking-stick Siu knew her mother was worried.
All night little Kuang had cried in his sleep.
This morning he was very hot. His face was red.
Siu, watching her mother and grandmother's faces,
knew that they were afraid. She had said nothing.
What could a crippled girl do? She was useless.
She wished that she were the sick one and her
brother well!

Walking-stick Siu thought of her brother now
as she picked a few flowers growing along the
river's edge. Would the flowers make him feel
better?

Slowly, she left her mother by the river and
with the flowers in one hand and her walking stick
in the other, she returned to the village.

Usually, her grandmother sat in front of their
house. Today, she was still inside, still in bed
when Siu entered. The room was hot and dark. It
smelled of sickness.

"I brought some flowers for Kuang," said Siu
softly.

"Flowers are no good," said her Grandmother
bitterly. "Someone must go to the old Waterfall
Monk and ask him what to do."

Walking-stick Siu knew about the old monk,
but she had never seen him. He never came to the
village, but lived by himself in a cave near a huge
waterfall. The waterfall, she'd heard told, was
taller than any building and made a terrible roar,
like a giant rushing monster. It frightened her
to think of the Waterfall Monk. Some said he
never talked. She wondered if that were true.

"Someone must go to him," her grandmother continued. "If your father were here, he would go."

Walking-stick Siu listened to her grandmother. She waited for her to go on, but now her grandmother was crying. Siu took her grandmother's hand, saying nothing. At last she asked, "If you follow the river will you come to the waterfall?"

"Yes," her grandmother said, "but all the men are gone."

Siu said nothing. She stroked her grandmother's hand and looked across at Kuang. His face was hot and feverish. Every now and then he cried out that he was thirsty, but he would not drink the cold stream water she brought him.

The sun was halfway up the sky when Siu's mother returned with the laundry. "There you are," she scolded. "I wondered where you had run off to this time. You are little enough help as it is not to cause me more trouble now!"

Siu's mother put down the laundry in the back courtyard. "Have you filled the water jug yet?" she called to Siu.

"No, mother."

"Go fill it now, you lazy girl." Walking-stick Siu took the jug and went to the village well. As she filled the jug, her eyes looked down to the river. Slowly, she looked up the river to where it rounded a forested hillside and disappeared into the mountains. It was a long way. She picked up the heavy jug and carried it home.

"You'll have to fill the wood box for Kuang today, too," said her mother as Siu put the jug by the door. Walking-stick Siu nodded and went out. The dark house with its sickness frightened her. She was glad to fill the wood box. As she worked, she looked again and again at the river. Now it did not seem so far to the mountains and surely, the old monk would know how to make her brother and grandmother well again. The thought made her happy. She worked harder. Soon the wood box was filled.

Her mother gave her a bowl of rice mixed with a few vegetables. Siu said nothing, but she could see that her mother was even more worried. Inside, she could hear her brother moaning. He was thirsty, but still he couldn't drink. Walking-stick Siu looked across the village, past the river, to where the river joined the mountains. No, she thought, it is not far. But could she walk that far? I'm not fast, she thought to herself, but I know how to keep going one step at a time.

The sun was high overhead when Walking-stick Siu left the village. She did not tell anyone where she was going. She knew they would not let her, a lame girl, go.

At first, Siu walked slowly. It was hard to keep walking. Never before had she left her village. She longed already to turn back, but scolded herself severely. "Siu," she said, "you lazy, good-for-nothing girl, you can't even do what you set out to do. What good are you!" And after this scolding, she went on without turning back.

As she walked along the wide cart path bordering the river, a flock of crows flew into a nearby tree. "Caw, caw," they said. Walking-stick Siu thought it sounded like, "Go back! Go back!" Their caws were so terrible she wanted to turn and run, but she had already told herself she would not turn back.

Walking-stick Siu stopped. She looked hard at the cawing crows. Three crows flew out of the tree straight at her.

Frightened, Siu waved her stick and arms. "Go away! Go away!" she said. The crows flew out of the tree straight at her.

Walking-stick Siu grew braver. "You are just the same crows who caw by the village," she called out. "You cannot frighten me. You are just silly old, noisy crows!"

The crows cawed back at her. Now it sounded to Siu like they said, "Go on! Go on!" Siu walked on.

The longer Siu walked in the afternoon sun along the river bank, the happier she became. The flock of crows accompanied her flying from tree to tree. Once, their loud cawing told her when a man with a great bundle of firewood on his back was coming along the path. Walking-stick Siu hid. She did not want anyone to stop her.

Along the river bank she saw the same red, yellow and blue flowers that grew by her village. An afternoon breeze blew bending the flowers as it passed. Siu thought it looked like they were waving at her. She hurried on now feeling happier than she had ever felt before.

The afternoon sun began to sink towards the western hills. Long shadows stretched from the trees across the path.   Songbirds sang their evening songs from rushes, branches, stumps and tree tops along the river path. Siu's stomach was empty. She was hungry now. She thought of her mother fixing dinner, calling her to come eat, discovering that she was gone.

Walking-stick Siu felt tired and discouraged. She had not known it would be so far to the Waterfall Monk's cave. She did not like to think of her mother worrying about her. Her poor mother had too many worries already with her brother and grandmother sick and her father gone. Maybe she should have stayed and helped. Maybe she should go back.

Siu turned and looked back. She was on the hillside now, following the river into the mountains. Siu was surprised to discover that she could see her village far off in the distance by the river. She could also see two other villages way off to the right. Siu had not known that the world was so big. She could not go back tonight. It was too far; besides she had not seen the Waterfall Monk.

Standing on the hillside, Walking-stick Siu watched the blazing red sun set. Clouds billowing up on the horizon turned pink, red, and yellow, then the colors faded as a deep purple dusk settled over the plains. Now Siu hurried. She must find a place to spend the night.

Walking-stick Siu limped faster along the path.
More clouds moved across the sky. The wind began
blowing harder, sighing through the trees.

Once Siu, nearly exhausted, stopped and tried
to fix herself a place under a large tree. But
the wind swirled around the tree's trunk and
through her thin clothing. As she lay shivering
on the ground, doubts arose. "What if there were
no old Waterfall Monk," the wind seemed to be saying. "Your grandmother is old. Perhaps, the old
Monk has died? Perhaps, there never was a Waterfall Monk?" the wind whispered into her ear. She
shook herself. "No. There is a Waterfall Monk."
Shivering, she pulled her garments around her.
Again the wind whispering through the tree above
her seemed to say--"You are a foolish girl to be-
lieve such stories." Then she heard the pitter
patter of rain-drops on the ground. "I can't stay
here," she thought. "I must go on."

It was dark now as Walking-stick Siu groped
her way slowly along the rough trail. Occasionally,
she stumbled in the dark, falling over a tree root
or boulder in the trail. The trail now was much
more difficult as it wound upward across the
forested hillside. Few people travelled into the
mountain wilderness. Walking-stick Siu had entered
into the deep forest. Below her she could hear
the rushing river. It was no longer the gentle,
slow stream that flowed past her village, but a
powerful mountain torrent full of life and vigor.
And tired and hungry though she was, Siu found

strength and joy in the roar of the fast flowing water. It did not frighten her, as some people said the mountain river would; it gave her the energy to go on, one step at a time, until she reached the top of the hill.

At first, Siu did not know what was ahead of her. In the dark night, she could only see that it was too big to be a rock and too small to be a hut. Slowly, she approached closer and closer.

As she drew near, the moon briefly appeared from behind a dark cloud. Before her was a very small, three-sided shed. Inside the shed someone had placed a white statue of Kuan Shih Yin Bodhisattva. The statue seemed to glow warm in the moonlight.

"Kuan Shih Yin," Siu cried with relief and joy. "You have come to help me." Tired and cold, she crawled into the little shed.

No sooner had Walking-stick Siu reached safety than it began to rain again, harder this time. Exhausted, Siu curled up at Kuan Shih Yin's feet and fell asleep listening to rain drops pounding on the roof.

Sometime during the night, the rain stopped. Siu woke as the sky began to lighten. Lying in the shed, she watched a songbird fly from the limb of a nearby tree to a bush, then to a large grey boulder in front of the shrine. Here he began singing his dawn song. Soon other birds joined his chorus as the first rays of sunlight stretched across the hilltop clearing to creep into the Kuan Shih Yin shrine, warming Siu's cold and stiff body.

She shivered; then when the birds had finished their morning song, Siu stretched and crawled out of the shrine. Standing before the white image of compassionate Kuan Shih Yin Bodhisattva, Siu made her morning bows.

Then, once again, Walking-stick Siu set out to reach the Old Monk by the waterfall. Her stomach growled. It had had nothing to eat. Her legs were stiff and sore from yesterday's long walk. She made them walk faster. Her feet and knees were cut and bruised from tripping and falling in the dark. She ignored them. Her heart was light, her spirits bounded eagerly forward. Below her she could see the trail descending into a small valley. At the head of the valley, the long silvery white line of the waterfall shimmered in the early morning light.

Slowly, Walking-stick Siu approached the Old Man sitting in front of his cave by the waterfall. Suddenly, she realized, she had brought nothing. Her hands were empty. What could she give him? Nothing. Would he help? Could he help?

Fear overtook her again. She wanted to run, to run back down the little valley, over the hill and through the deep forest down the path along the river's edge that led to her village. Oh, if only she could run! How fast she would run away. She had never before spoken to a stranger.

But Walking-stick Siu could not run. "I've come this far," she thought. "I have been through the dark woods and slept in the wilderness. I cannot turn back. My brother and grandmother need my help."

Slowly, Siu put one foot in front of the other. Now, she was standing before him. "I can bow," she thought. Walking-stick Siu made three bows before the Old Monk. When she finished, she sat down to wait, respectfully.

The Old Man sat quietly. Siu waited. She watched a yellow and black butterfly fly from a warm pebble up to a clump of white flowers. The flowers were different, she noticed, from the ones by her village. The trees were different, too.

Still, the old man sat. "Maybe he doesn't want visitors," she thought. "Maybe I should go

For a long time the Waterfall Monk looked quietly, kindly at Sui. Then nodding, he motioned for her to leave.

away." She glanced at him. He was deep in meditation, yet Siu knew he wanted her to stay. She
sat quietly, waiting.

A warm morning breeze blew up from the valley
full of fragrant scents of many trees and flowers.
It stirred his black robes and ruffled her hair.
Nearby, the waterfall danced over the rocks with
unending life and vigor.

Suddenly, Walking-stick Siu noticed the Old
Monk beckoning for her to speak. She coughed,
shyly, then began speaking. "Oh Venerable One.
I have come from Yu-yen Village. My father has
gone to work on the Emperor's new road. My brother
and grandmother are ill. They are hot, but cannot
drink. They are tired and weak, but cannot sleep.
All day and night they cry and moan. Many people
in my village are sick, too. My grandmother said
you would know what to do."

The Old Monk listened. When Walking-stick
Siu finished, he sat quietly for many minutes, then
slowly he got up. Siu watched. He turned and motioned for her to follow. Silently, breathlessly,
Siu followed him into his great cave. They passed
through the outer room into a smaller back cave.
The Old Monk lit a torch. The walls of the cave
were hung with dried flowers, leaves, bark and
roots of many plants. Some Siu thought she recog-
nized, but others she did not.

The old Waterfall Monk swung the torch search-
ing up and down the walls, looking at each clump
of dried herbs. At last, his light stopped on a
small cluster. Slowly and carefully, he lifted it

off the wall. Holding it in his ancient hand, he walked to the mouth of the cave. Walking-stick Siu followed. In the daylight, he pointed to the small flowers at the end of the stalk, then to the blue sky. Siu thought, it has blue flowers. He showed her how the twigs all branched off from the stalk, alternately, first from one side, then from the other. Yes, I have noticed that some plants do that, Siu thought, but others are different. He showed her about how high the bush grew with his old, wrinkled hand. Then he turned, walked back into the cave and hung the herbs back on the wall.

Tears welled up in Siu's eyes. She had come so far. Surely, he would give her some. He didn't mean to send her home empty-handed, did he? Bravely, she blinked fast and waited patiently to see what the strange, old Waterfall Monk would do next.

He picked up a cooking pot and gathered a handful of rice from a sack. Turning to Siu, he motioned her to get firewood. They would eat.

Walking-stick Siu hurried as fast as she could to get firewood. Soon the rice was boiling. The Old Monk tossed in some wild greens and dried herbs. Siu did not recognize them. She didn't care. She was so hungry that her stomach hurt. Now it seemed like days since she had eaten, not just yesterday noon.

They ate together in the warm, early morning sunshine. Siu thought it was the best meal she had ever had.

When they were finished, the Old Monk beckoned to her again, this time pointing back the way she had come and then to the right. Walking-stick Siu thought, "He wants me to go someplace. But where? How can I find this place?" He indicated the herb room and then again gestured quietly pointing back along the route she had come and then to the right.

"I'm to go find that plant," she thought. "How can I?" No sooner had this doubt occurred, than Siu thought, "Yes, I can. I have come this far. I have done things I have never done before. I have been places I have never been before. With his help, I can find the plant and collect my own herbs."

Walking-stick Siu bowed to the Old Monk, then started back down the trail. Suddenly, she remembered a little pathway, hardly more than a faint animal's trail, that went off to the right. She had noticed it this morning, but passed it by on her way to the waterfall. Now she would try that trail.

The pathway wandered up another hillside covered with clumps of tall trees growing between rocky cliffs on which grew thick clumps of ferns and rich green mosses. Walking-stick Siu climbed slowly looking at all the plants for a bush with blue flowers. At first, she looked just beside the trail, but as she climbed higher and still had not found the bush, she started looking farther and farther from the pathway. She searched in a meadow filled with fragrant blue and yellow wild flowers, but there were no blue flowering bushes. She looked along the slippery banks of a stream overhung with towering white cluster-flowers and smaller, brilliant orange and black flowers. She

climbed over fallen trees and squeezed through
thickets of prickling thorns, but no blue flowering bushes grew there. She walked under huge,
towering trees whose great round limbs blotted out
the sun leaving the ground below dark. No flowers
or bushes grew beneath them. Beyond the trees,
she could see a rocky ledge warmed by the mid-
morning sun. Walking-stick Siu stepped out of the
woods onto the great rock ledge. The rock was
bigger than any she had ever seen. It seemed to
stretch for miles. On three sides the woods grew
right up to the rock, but on the fourth side, the
rock seemed to fall away into the valley below.
Siu felt as if she were standing on the edge of
the world. Yesterday, back in the village, she
would have been frightened. Today, she wasn't.
The rock was warm. Many plants grew in its cracks
and crevices.

Across the middle of the rock ran a giant
crack. A lizard was sunning himself by the crack,
but Siu did not see him. Siu saw a small bush
with blue flowers growing out of the crack. As
quickly as she could, she limped across the rock.
Her heart pounded. Was this it? Sitting down
beside the bush, she examined it carefully. Blue
flowers, tiny leaves, alternating branches, yes,
it looked the same. Siu picked a few branches and
put them into the small bag the Old Monk had given
her. Then, looking around the rock more carefully,
she spotted other, similar bushes. In the future,
she thought, she'd know where to come for them.

Happy, Siu returned once more to the old Waterfall Monk's cave. The fire was still going. The

Old Monk remained silent, but looked pleased at her return and gave her his nodding approval when she showed him the branches. Taking a very small twig with leaves and flowers, he dropped it into boiling water. Siu sat and watched. She wanted to go home now as soon as possible, but she knew the Old Monk was not ready for her to leave. Siu sat patiently, waiting, watching, learning. At home, she would make the tea for her brother and grandmother. Siu looked at the bag. She could even make tea for the whole village. For this, Siu could wait. She sat, saying nothing, quietly waiting for the tea to brew.

After what seemed like a very long time, but was probably only a few minutes, the Old Monk removed the pot from the fire setting it to cool on a flat stone. From the cave he brought out two tea bowls. Carefully, he poured a little herbal tea into each bowl, then beckoned for Siu to take one.

Siu picked up her bowl holding it between both hands as she saw the Old Monk doing. Slowly, he moved the bowl back and forth sniffing the rising steam. Siu did likewise. Its spicy odor tingled her nose and filled her lungs. "I'm not sick," she thought, "but I feel better anyway!"

When the medicinal tea had cooled, the Venerable Old One taught her to moisten her lips, then to sip it slowly with long pauses between the tiny sips. Siu watched carefully doing and remembering every detail, exactly.

Once again the sun hung high overhead. The Old Monk put down his empty tea bowl. For a long

time he looked quietly, kindly at Siu, then nodding
he motioned for her to leave. Siu rose, bowed,
took up her precious bag and started down the trail.
Not until she had climbed the hill and stopped to
bow to the Kuan Shih Yin shrine did Siu remember
her walking stick. "Oh well, I can limp along
fine on two legs," she said to herself. "I hope the
Waterfall Monk uses my walking stick for firewood,"
and laughing, she headed down the long hill through
the forest to the cart path along the river.

"Someone's coming! Someone's coming!" children's voices called out ringing through the village.
"Where?"
"Where?"
"Along the river trail."
"Which way?" asked Siu's mother coming out of
their house.
"Which way?" cried the children back to the
look-out.
"From the mountains, from the mountains, from
the mountains," came the calling voices.
Other mothers appeared. Everyone knew, but
no one believed the Grandmother's feverish story
that Siu had gone to the mountains to get medicine
from the Waterfall Monk. Everyone knew that only
men and boys went to the mountains. Not girls,
not Walking-stick Siu. "She has run off," said
her mother. "She was lazy and afraid of the sickness." "She's fallen in the river," said other
mothers. "Bandits have taken her," said some of
the children, although no one had seen any bandits

for years.

But now, someone was coming. Could it really be Walking-stick Siu? Children poured out of the village. Every child well enough to run was running down the cart path towards the approaching figure.

Siu's mother did not. She had two sick ones to care for. She could wait to see if it were Siu. Maybe Siu had tried foolishly to go to the mountains. She wasn't sure how far it was, but she knew Siu couldn't go that far. She had given up and come home. Stupid girl. It was bad enough to run off and leave her mother alone to care for the sick ones with no one to fetch water and firewood or feed the chickens or weed the garden. But to set out to get help then quit was even worse. Her daughter was a disgrace. A good for nothing. She wouldn't go out to meet her.

"It's Siu. It's Siu," rang the voices through the village.

"Siu's been to the Waterfall Monk."

"Siu has medicine."

Siu's mother opened the door. Up the village path came the village children and many mothers. In their midst walked Siu carrying a small bag.

"Siu," cried her mother. "Where is your walking stick. You'll fall and hurt yourself."

"I don't need it any more, mother. I'm slow, but I can walk on two legs. I have been to the Waterfall Monk's cave. In my bag I have medicinal herbs to cure the sick."

"Give it to me, Siu, and I will fix it."

Siu stopped. "No, mother. The Old Monk

showed me how to fix it and how it should be sipped.
I can show everyone."

"You're just a girl. What do you know about
these things. Don't talk-back. Give me the bag."

"Wait, Mrs. Liang," said a mother. "We all
know Siu, but she has changed. This is not Walking-
stick Siu, but Siu-the-healer. See how much better
she walks. Let her show us how the Waterfall Monk
fixed the tea."

Siu's mother stopped. She looked bewildered,
unsure. The girl standing before her was Siu, but
she was different. In her heart, she knew Siu had
changed, yet it was still hard to realize it. Yes,
the other mothers were right. She was no longer
her little, Walking-stick Siu, but Siu-the-healer.
Slowly, Siu's mother nodded her agreement and
gently began to cry. Her tears were tears of joy
and happiness mixed with tears of sadness and loss.

HOW PEOPLE CAME TO BE ON THE EARTH

When our planet was very, very new and there were no living beings on it yet, some gods from the Light-Sound Heaven came down to earth. At that time there was no sun, moon, or stars. There was no day or night. There were no years, no months, and no spring, summer, fall, and winter.

The gods of the Light-Sound Heaven had their own light on their bodies and they could also fly. Back and forth they flitted between the Light-Sound Heaven and this new earth they had found. At that time the gods didn't need to actually put food in their mouths and eat it in order to get full. All they had to do was think about what they would like to eat and they would be full. They lived without eating in the way that you and I are accustomed to. They took happy thoughts as their food.

These gods began to refer to themselves as "living beings." It is from that time onward that there came to be such a thing as "living beings." Eventually the term broadened to include any sentient creature which had blood and breath.

THE GODS BEGAN TO EAT

When the gods came down to our earth, they found something which they named the "fat of the land " growing all around. When some of the more adventuresome gods saw the "fat of the land" growing up all around, they couldn't resist the temptation of sticking their fingers into the sweet, buttery rich substance. Once they'd stuck their fingers in it, they licked their fingers and found that it tasted as good as it looked. It was so sweet and rich, in fact, that they couldn't stop sampling it. When their companions saw them eating it, they wanted to try it too. Soon all the gods got greedy for the "fat of the land" and ate more and more of it.

Originally their bodies had been extremely light-weight as well as capable of constantly emitting a pure light. That was because they didn't eat anything in the way that you and I are accustomed to. But when they began to consume the "fat of the land" by putting it in their mouths and swallowing it, they began to get heavy and fat. They started to develop muscles and soon they got so heavy that they could no longer fly. They could only walk around on the earth. Also, their bodies didn't emit that pure light any more.

Because their bodies stopped emitting light, there came to be a sun and a moon and stars in the sky above them. Once there was a sun, then the earth began to rotate on its axis and day and night came to be. The moon began to revolve around the earth and one full rotation of it marked a period of time called a month. The earth then began to revolve around the sun and each single revolution of it marked a period called a year.

Meanwhile the gods who ate more of the "fat of the land" became ugly and the gods who ate less retained more of their beauty. So for the first time, a distinction became evident between those who were handsome and those who were ugly.

The handsome ones looked down on the ugly ones
and the ugly ones were jealous of those who were
handsome.

Because of these distinctions, they started
fighting and quite soon after their quarreling
began, the sweet, rich "fat of the land" disappeared. It was replaced by a lesser variety of
"fat of the land," which was not as sweet and rich
as that first kind had been. But it caused the
same change to take place in the living beings.
Those who were greedy and ate a lot of it became
quite ugly. Those who ate less of it retained
some of their godlike beauty. Once again the
ugly ones grew jealous of the beautiful ones and
the lovely ones looked down on the ugly ones.
More fights broke out and with that, the second
variety of "fat of the land" disappeared.

It was replaced by another "fat of the land,"
but this variety was not as good and tasty as
the one that had just disappeared. Its effect was
the same, however. It caused those who ate a lot
of it to turn ugly. Those who were not as greedy
and who did not eat as much of the fat of the
land, remained more beautiful than those greedy
ones. The ugly ones grew jealous of the lovely
ones and the beautiful ones looked down on the
ugly ones. This led to more quarrelling and
the third kind of "fat of the land " disappeared
from the face of the earth.

The third kind of "fat of the land" was replaced by a kind of grain that began growing up
from the earth. This grain was of superior quality
in that it didn't have hulls and it didn't need

to be cooked before it could be eaten. It could just be picked and consumed.

Up to this point, there had been no distinction between men and women. Everyone had been the same. But once they began eating this grain, people began to change and divide into two kinds. People with more emotion became women and people with less emotion became men. They began to look at each other and gradually this caused them to have emotion and desire. Then they liked being together with each other. But then some of the more beautiful gods, who had not indulged in so much "fat of the land" and who had not yet consumed the grain, scolded the men and women. "What you are doing is wrong." The men felt very ashamed. They threw themselves on the ground. They did not want to do anything.

Then the women brought the men some food to eat. They did not want the men to starve. The men began to call the women who brought them food their wives. That is how there came to be the term "husbands and wives."

The gods who had not yet eaten the grains didn't think that the marriages between the men and women were proper, so they told them to leave. The men and women went away for three months, and then they came back to join the other living beings. By the time they returned, the other living beings had eaten enough of the grain to be aware of the distinction between men and women, too. From that time on, no one thought that having husbands and wives was improper.

Originally, when the gods first came to earth,

they didn't live in houses. But now, those who had become men and women started building houses because they felt ashamed. From that time on, people in the world always lived in some kind of shelter. Before they ate the grain, they had always been born by transformation. But now that they had become men and women, they gave birth to their children from the women's wombs. That was the beginning of the term "womb".

A LAZY IDEA

Originally when the men and women were hungry they would go out and collect enough food to satisfy their hunger. But some of the lazy ones decided that if they collected a lot of food all at once, then they wouldn't have to go out every time they felt hungry. Pretty soon someone said to one of these lazy people, "Let's go gather some food now."

The lazy person replied, "Oh, I already got some yesterday, so I don't need to go out today."

"That's a really smart idea!" replied the other person. "That's a good way to do it."

Pretty soon they all started going out and gathering more than they needed for one meal. They took enough to last for two or three days at a time. Eventually people were gathering a five-day food supply, all at the same time.

Originally when they picked the grain it would grow back all by itself again, but what do you suppose happened once they got their lazy idea? As soon as they all started picking too much at once, the grain didn't grow back any more. It all disappeared.

Another kind of grain replaced it, but this grain was covered with hulls. It had to be threshed and winnowed and processed before it could be eaten. It also had to be cooked. It didn't grow as fast as the first kind of grain had. Since all this attention was necessary to cultivate the grain, people began to divide up the land. Using a map, they marked off divisions and made decisions. "This is mine and that is yours." That is when the term "field" came into existence. And what do you suppose happened when people began thinking of things as being "mine" and "yours"?

When one person's field didn't produce enough, that person would steal grain from someone else's field. The person stolen from would attack the person who stole his grain and so fighting broke out again. There was so much strife that the people decided they needed someone to mediate. They needed a judge to watch over them and decide who was right and who was wrong. They chose a tall, handsome individual who had some virtue and they gave him some food as payment for arbitrating their fights. That individual became known as the "king."

At first the kings were all very virtuous. They all held the Five Precepts. They were Wheel-Turning Kings who were benevolent to the people. But eventually kings began to reign who were not virtuous and who did not benefit the people.

THE LIFE-SPAN GETS SHORTER

Up until that time, the life-span of the people
had been very long. It was 84,000 years on the average. But when they began to steal and to hurt
one another, their life-spans decreased to an average
of 40,000 years in length. It was about this time
that their bodies changed so they became flesh and
blood and they became more earthbound. As their
bad deeds and harming acts increased, their life-
spans decreased to 20,000 years.

They continued to get greedier and greedier
and to fight more and more over what things belonged
to whom. They wanted more and more food. This
caused their life-spans to decrease to 10,000 years.

Up to this point, although they had stolen from
each other and harmed one another, no one had yet
told a lie. But one day when a thief got caught
and brought before the king, the king said, "Did
you steal that from him?"

The thief thought to himself, "If I say I did
steal it, I'm going to be punished. I don't want
to be punished, so I'll say I didn't." That is how
lies came into being. Once the thieves started
saying "No, I didn't steal that from him," their
life-spans decreased until they were only 1,000
years in length.

At this point, people began to do three bad
things. They started to use "double-tongued"
speech. That means they would say one thing to a
person's face and something different behind
his back. They started using harsh speech, which

means they would swear and yell at each other.
And then they started gossiping. Once these three
evils took hold, their life-spans decreased to
500 years.

At this point, people began to do impure
things and have all sorts of improper conduct
and deviant views. They no longer knew right from
wrong.

SHAKYAMUNI BUDDHA ENTERS THE WORLD

When the people's life-spans reached an average of 100 years, Shakyamuni Buddha appeared in
the world. That was about 3,000 years ago. Once
the Buddha was in the world, he taught people the
Proper Dharma. He taught them to do good things.
However, people's life-spans have continued to
decrease, because most people continue to do bad
things anyway.

THE FUTURE

But the Dharma which the Buddha taught will
gradually leave the world, and as that happens
people will do worse and worse things and their
life-spans will therefore get shorter and shorter.
Every 100 years their life-spans will get shorter
by one year. This will continue until people get
so bad that they will only have a life-span of
ten years. At that time girls will be able to
marry and bear children when they are only five
months old. People's heights will also get
shorter and shorter. They will have no virtue.
There will be no good in the world.

THE EARTH BECOMES UGLY

There will be nothing of beauty in the world.
There will be nothing sweet and pleasant to eat
left. All the grains will disappear because people
will have used them all up. If a grain of rice
were to be found at that time, it would be so
valuable that it would be locked up as a treasure.
It would be as precious as jewels are to us now.

Because there will be so much killing, the
earth will become laden with human bones and flesh.
Since people have nothing else to eat, they will
begin eating the earth itself which contains these
human remains. Since there will be nothing to make
clothing from, people will use the human hair of
the dead to make their clothing. Their outer
garments will be made from a kind of coarse,
scratchy wool.

The earth itself will be so depleted that
it will not bear crops. Only stones and rocks and
thorns will abound. However mosquitoes, wasps, and
poisonous snakes will multiply and bother the people.

No gold, silver, lapis lazuli or other jewels
will remain. No one will ever hear about the Ten
Good Deeds. (No killing, no stealing, no sexual
misconduct, no greed, no hatred, no stupidity,
no double-tongued speech, no harsh speech, no
loose speech, and no lying). No one will be filial
to their parents or respectful of their teachers
and elders. People will only do bad things at
this time. They will have so much anger inside
them that as soon as they see someone else they
will want to kill the other person. That will cause

everyone to be afraid of everyone else. Everyone will be afraid that someone is going to kill them.

THE SEVEN-DAY WAR

Finally, an horrendous war will ensue. People's karma will be so bad that they won't even need to use weapons to kill each other. They will just pick blades of grass and use those to kill each other.

But some people will be afraid of what is happening. They won't want to fight in the war. They will run away to the mountains and will feel a small change take place in their hearts. Those who go to the mountains will get together and make an agreement: "If you won't hurt me, I won't hurt you." Out of fear, some will retreat to isolated islands, some will hide away in mountain caves.

After seven days they will come down from the mountains and discover that the Seven-day War is over and that all the people who did not go to the mountains died in that war, leaving a total number of only 10,000 people in the whole world. Discovering this, the mountain people will feel so sad that they will cry for seven days because of all the people who were killed in the war. But then they will rejoice for seven days because they still have each other.

PEOPLE BRING FORTH THEIR TRUE HEARTS

At that time they will decide, "From now on we're going to do good deeds and benefit one another. We will not do any of those terrible things which lead people to kill one another.

We will not kill each other any more." Once they vow not to kill, their life-spans will increase from ten to twenty years.

Then they'll think, "If I steal someone else's things, then someone else will steal mine. It will go on and on like this, until no one will feel safe and secure. I should stop stealing." Once they stop stealing, their life-spans will increase to 40 years.

Then they will begin to think, "All older men and women are like my own father and mother, and all young boys and girls are like my brothers and sisters, so I should respect them and I should respect myself, too, and not do impure things." When they stop doing impure things with one another, their life-spans will increase to 80 years.

Before too long they will realize that they should not lie to each other, either. And once' they stop lying their life-spans will increase to 160 years.

Their hearts will grow in kindness and they will want all people to be at peace with one another, and so they will vow not to use double-tongued speech any more. Once they do that their life-spans will increase to 320 years.

Then they will stop using harsh speech. They will not say unkind things to one another. They will use kind words instead. Once that happens, their life-span will increase to 640 years.

When they stop gossiping their life-spans will increase to 2000 years. When they stop being stingy, their life-spans will increase to 5000 years. When they stop being jealous, their life-spans will increase to 10,000 years. When

they stop having deviant views and start having
proper views, their life-spans will increase to
20,000 years. When their life-spans get to be
40,000 years, they will decide to be filial to their
parents. Once they begin being filial, their life-
spans will double--increasing to 80,000 years.

At that time girls will not be able to marry
and bear children until they are 500 years old.
Their childhood will last for 500 years. Everyone
will be very healthy. Only nine diseases will
remain.

THE NINE DISEASES

1. People may get too cold.
2. People may get too hot.
3. People may feel hungry.
4. People may feel thirsty.
5. People may have to urinate.
6. People may have to defecate.
7. People may have desire.
8. People may eat too much.
9. People will still eventually get old.

MAITREYA BUDDHA

Other than those nine problems, there will be
no other difficulties. The world will be very
beautiful. There will be many jewels and precious
things. The flies, mosquitoes and poisonous creatures will have disappeared. Everyone will have
plenty of food to eat. People's life-spans will
increase to a maximum of 84,000 years. Then they
will gradually begin to decrease again. When

people's life-spans decrease to 80,000 years, they
will still enjoy all these wonderful things--a
beautiful world to live in, good food to eat, har-
monious relationships with one another, and clothing and gems in abundance. At that time Maitreya
Buddha, the next Buddha after Shakyamuni Buddha
to come to this world, will appear.

"If you won't hurt me, I won't hurt you."

THE BUDDHIST TEXT TRANSLATION SOCIETY

CHAIRPERSON: The Venerable Tripitaka Master Hsüan Hua
             -Abbot of Gold Mountain Monastery,
              Gold Wheel Temple, and Tathagata Monastery
             -Chancellor of Dharma Realm Buddhist
              University
             -Professor of the Tripitaka and the Dhyanas

PRIMARY TRANSLATION COMMITTEE:

Chairpersons: Bhikshuni Heng Hsien
              Bhikshuni Heng Ch'ih

Members:

Bhikshu Heng Sure   Bhikshuni Heng Wen
Bhikshu Heng Kuan   Bhikshuni Heng Tao
Bhikshu Heng Shun   Bhikshuni Heng Jieh
Bhikshu Heng Tso   Bhikshuni Heng Ming
Bhikshu Heng Deng   Shramanerika Heng Tsai
Bhikshu Heng Kung   Shramanerika Heng Duan
Bhikshu Heng Wu   Shramanerika Heng Bin
Bhikshuni Heng Ch'ing   Shramanerika Heng Chia
Bhikshuni Heng Chü   Shramanerika Heng Liang
Bhikshuni Heng Chai   Upasaka Kuo Jung (R.B.) Epstein
Upasika Kuo Ts'an Nicholson Upasaka Kuo Li (Li-jen) Chou
Upasaka Kuo Chou Rounds

REVIEWING COMMITTEE:

Chairpersons: Bhikshu Heng Tso
              Upasaka Kuo Jung Epstein

Members:

Bhikshu Heng Sure   Bhikshuni Heng Chai
Bhikshu Heng Kuan   Bhikshuni Heng Wen
Bhikshu Heng Deng   Bhikshuni Heng Tao
Bhikshu Heng Gung   Shramanerika Heng Tsai
Bhikshu Heng Wu   Shramanerika Heng Duan
Bhikshuni Heng Hsien   Upasaka Kuo Jung Epstein
Bhikshuni Heng Ch'ih   Upasika Hsien Ping-ying
Upasika Kuo Ts'an Nicholson Upasaka Kuo Chou Rounds
Upasika Kuo Chin Vickers   Upasaka Chou Kuo Li
Upasika Phuong Kuo Wu

Dharma Protector Wei To Bodhisattva

Verse of Transference

May the merit and virtue accrued from this work,
Adorn the Buddhas' Pure Lands,
Repaying four kinds of kindness above,
And aiding those suffering·in the paths below.

May those who see and hear of this.
All bring forth the resolve for Bodhi,
And when this retribution body is over,
Be born together in ultimate bliss.

All BTTS translations include extensive inter-linear commentary by the Venerable Tripitaka Master Hsuan Hua, unless otherwise noted. All works available in
softcover only unless otherwise noted.
ISBN Prefix: 0-917512

SUTRAS (Scriptures spoken by the Buddha):

AMITABHA SUTRA - Explains the causes and circumstances
for rebirth in the Land of Ultimate Bliss of Amitabha
Buddha. 01-4, 204 pgs., $8.00. (Also available in
Spanish. $8.00)

BRAHMA NET SUTRA - Vol. I contains the Ten Major Precepts,
and the first Twenty Minor Precepts. English/Chinese.
79-0, 300 pgs., $10.00.
   Vol. II - The Twenty-first Minor Precept through the
   Forty-Eighth Minor Precept. English/Chinese. 88-X,
   210 pgs., $8.00.
   Entire text only is also available. 56-1, $5.00.

DHARANI SUTRA - Tells of the past events in the life of
the Bodhisattva of Great Compassion, Avalokiteshvara
(Kuan Yin). It explains the meaning of the mantra line
by line, and contains Chinese poems and drawings of division bodies of Kuan Yin for each of the 84 lines of the
mantra. Drawings and verses on each of the 42 Hands and
Eyes of Kuan Yin. 13-8, 352 pgs., $12.00.

千手千眼大悲心陀羅尼經 - DHARANI SUTRA - Original
Chinese text only. 210 pgs., $6.00.

DHARMA FLOWER (LOTUS) SUTRA- This Sutra, spoken in the
last period of the Buddha's teaching, proclaims the ulti-
mate principles of the Dharma which unites all previous
teachings into one. The following are volumes which
have been published to date:
   VOL. I INTRODUCTION.
   VOL. II INTRODUCTION, CHAPTER ONE.
   VOL. III EXPEDIENT METHODS, CHAPTER TWO.
   VOL. IV A PARABLE, CHAPTER THREE.
   VOL. V BELIEF AND UNDERSTANDING, CHAPTER FOUR.
   VOL. VI MEDICINAL HERBS, CHAPTER FIVE, and CON-
   FERRING PREDICTIONS, CHAPTER SIX.
   VOL. VII PARABLE OF THE TRANSFORMATION CITY,
   CHAPTER SEVEN.
   VOL. VIII FIVE HUNDRED DISCIPLES RECEIVE PRE-
   DICTIONS, CHAPTER EIGHT, and BESTOWING PREDIC-
   TIONS UPON THOSE STUDYING AND BEYOND STUDY,
   CHAPTER NINE.
   VOL. IX THE DHARMA MASTER, CHAPTER TEN, and
   VISION OF THE JEWELED STUPA, CHAPTER II.
   VOL. X DEVADATTA, CHAPTER TWELVE. Coming Soon.

FLOWER ADORNMENT (AVATAMSAKA) SUTRA VERSE PREFACE
清涼國師 華嚴經序送擇), a succinct verse commentary by T'ang
Dynasty National Master Ch'ing Liang (the Master of seven
emperors), which gives a complete overview of all the fun-
damental principles contained in the Sutra in eloquent
style. First English translation. BI-LINGUAL EDITION
Chinese and English. 244 pgs., 28-6, $7.00.

FLOWER ADORNMENT SUTRA PROLOGUE. A detailed explanation
of the principles of the Sutra utilizing the Hsien Shou
method of analyzing scriptures known as the Ten Doors,
by National Master Ch'ing Liang. The following volumes
have been published to date:

VOL. I, THE FIRST DOOR: THE CAUSES AND CONDITIONS FOR THE ARISAL OF THE TEACHING. 252 pgs., p.66-9 $10.00.
VOL. II, THE SECOND DOOR: THE STORES AND TEACHINGS TO WHICH IT BELONGS. PART ONE. 280 pgs., 73-1, $10.00.

清凉国师 華嚴經疏淺釋 entirety of the *AVATAMSAKA SUTRA PROLOGUE*, from First to Tenth Door, together with interlinear commentary by Ven. Abbot Hua, in four Volumes. CHINESE $5.00, $8.50, $8.50, and $5.00.

FLOWER ADORNMENT SUTRA - Known as the king of kings of all Buddhist scriptures because of its great length, (81 rolls containing more than 700,000 Chinese characters), and its profundity; it contains the most complete explanation of the Buddha's state and the Bodhisattva's quest for Awakening. When completed, the entire Sutra text with commentary is estimated to be from 75 to 100 volumes. The following volumes have been published to date:

> *FLOWER STORE SEA OF ADORNED WORLDS, CHAPTER 5, PART I. Available Soon.*
> *BRIGHT ENLIGHTENMENT, CHAPTER 9. Available Soon.*
> *PURE CONDUCT, CHAPTER 11. Available Soon.*
> *TEN DWELLINGS, CHAPTER 15.* 77-4, 185 pgs., $8.00.
> *BRAHMA CONDUCT, CHAPTER 16.* 80-4, 65 pgs., $4.00.
> *THE MERIT AND VIRTUE FROM FIRST BRINGING FORTH THE MIND, CHAPTER 17.* 83-9, 200 pgs., $7.00.
> *TEN INEXHAUSTIBLE TREASURIES, CHAPTER 22.* 38-3, 184 pgs., $7.00.
> *PRAISES IN THE TUSHITA HEAVEN PALACE, CHAPTER 24.* 39-1.
> *TEN TRANSFERENCES, CHAPTER 25, PART I. Available Soon.*
> *TEN GROUNDS, CHAPTER 26, PART I.* 87-1, 234 pgs, $7.00.
> *TEN GROUNDS, CHAPTER 26, PART II.* 74-X, 200 pgs., $8.00.

華嚴經十地品淺釋 The Second to the Tenth Grounds, contains the Bodhisattva's successive certification to each of the Sagely Grounds. CHINESE only. Grounds Two to Five in one volume now available; remaining Grounds forthcoming.

ENTERING THE DHARMA REALM, CHAPTER 39. This chapter relates the spiritual journey of the Youth Good Wealth in his search for Ultimate Awakening. In his quest he meets fifty-three "Good Teachers," each of whom represents a successive stage on the Bodhisattva path. The following volumes have been published to date:

PART 1. Describes the setting for the Youth's quest, and his meeting with Manjushri Bodhisattva. 280 pgs., 68-5, $8.50.

PART 2. Good Wealth meets his first ten teachers, who represent the positions of the Ten Dwellings. 250 pgs., 73-1, $8.50.

PART 3. The ten teachers who correspond to the levels of the Ten Conducts. 250 pgs., 73-1, $8.50.

PART 4. The ten teachers who represent the First to Sixth Grounds. 300 pgs., 81-2, $9.00.

PART 5. The four teachers who represent the Seventh to Tenth Grounds of a Bodhisattva. Available December, 1982.

HEART SUTRA AND VERSES WITHOUT A STAND - The text explains the meaning of Prajna Paramita, the perfection of wisdom. Each line in the Sutra is accompanied by an eloquent verse by the Ven. Abbot Hua. 160 pgs., 28-7, $7.50.

般若波羅蜜多心經非台頌解 same as above, including the commentary. IN CHINESE. 120 pgs., $5.00.

SHURANGAMA SUTRA - This Sutra, which reveals the Shurangama Samadhi and which contains the Shurangama Mantra,
primarily concerns the mind.

> VOL. I. Seven locations of the mind are all refuted.
> 289 pgs., 17-0, $8.50.

> VOL. II. Ten aspects of seeing; individual and col-
> lective karma. 212 pgs., 25-1, $8.50.

> VOL. III. Six sense organs, objects and conscious-
> nesses and seven elements. 240 pgs., 94-4, $8.50.

> VOL. IV. Continuity of world, living beings and
> karmic retribution. 200 pgs., 90-1, $8.50.

> VOL. V. Twenty-five sages tell of their perfect pene-
> tration. Kuan Yin Bodhisattva's method is selected
> by Manjushri Bodhisattva as most appropriate for peo-
> ple in this world. 250 pgs., 91-X, $8.50.

> VOL. VI. Four Clear and Unalterable Aspects of Puri-
> ty, the Bodhimanda, the Mantra, the Twelve Categories
> of Living Beings. 200 pgs., 97-9, $8.50.

> VOL. VII. Fifty-five stages of Bodhisattvahood and
> seven destinies. 270 pgs., $9.00.

> VOL. VIII. Fifty skandha demon states described in
> detail. FINAL VOLUME.

SIXTH PATRIARCH'S SUTRA - One of the foremost scriptures
of Ch'an (Zen) Buddhism, this text describes the life
and teachings of the remarkable Patriarch of the T'ang
Dynasty, Great Master Hui Neng. 235 pgs., 19-7, $10.00.
(Hardcover, $15.00).

SUTRA IN FORTY-TWO SECTIONS - This Sutra, the first to
be transported from India and translated into Chinese,
gives the most essential instructions in cultivating
the Dharma, emphasizing the cardinal virtues of renun-
ciation, contentment, and patience. 114 pgs., 15-4,
$4.00.

SUTRA OF THE PAST VOWS OF EARTH STORE BODHISATTVA -
This Sutra tells how Earth Store Bodhisattva attained
his position as one of the greatest Bodhisattvas, foremost in vows, and also describes the workings of karma,
how beings undergo rebirth, and the various kinds of
hells. Hardcover only, 235 pgs., 09-X, $16.00.

VAJRA PRAJNA PARAMITA (DIAMOND) SUTRA - the Vajra Sūtra
explains how the Bodhisattva relies on the Perfection
of Wisdom to teach and transform beings. 192 pgs.,
02-2, $8.00.

COMMENTARIAL LITERATURE:

BUDDHA ROOT FARM - A collection of lectures given during
an Amitabha Buddha recitation session which explains
practice and philosophy of the Pure Land School. 72
pgs., 08-1, $4.00.

CITY OF TEN THOUSAND BUDDHAS DAILY RECITATION HANDBOOK
萬佛城日誦儀規 contains all the material covered in the
traditional morning, afternoon, and evening services
and special services, recited daily in Buddhist mona-
steries in both East and West. Includes scriptures,
praises, chants, mantras, repentances, and so forth.
BI-LINGUAL. Chinese and English.

DOOR TO UNDERSTANDING THE 100 DHARMAS SHASTRAS. Available
Soon.

LISTEN TO YOURSELF, THINK IT OVER - Instruction on how
to practice the method of reciting the name of the
Bodhisattva of Great Compassion, Avalokiteshvara (Kuan
Yin), and an explanation of how to cultivate Ch'an (Zen)
meditation. 153 pgs., 24-3, $7.00.

One Heart Bowing to the City of 10,000 Buddhas

VOL. 1 - May 6 to June 30, 1977; 180 pgs., 21-9, $6.00.

VOL. 11 - July 1 to October 30, 1977; 322 pgs, 23-5, $7.50.

VOL. 111- October 30 to December 16, 1977; 154 pgs., 89-8, $6.00.

VOL. 1V - December 17, 1977 to January 21, 1978; 136 pgs., 90-1, $5.00.

VOL. V - January 22 to February 18, 1978; 127 pgs., 91-X, $5.00.

VOL. V1 - February 19, 1978 to April 2, 1978; 200 pgs., 92-8, $6.00.

VOL. VII -April 3, 1978 to May 24, 1978; 168 pgs.; 99-5.

Other volumes to appear in sequence, including the journals from the continuation of "Three Steps One Bow" within the City of 10,000 Buddhas, still in progress to date.

修行者的消息 - NEWS FROM TWO CULTIVATORS - LETTERS OF THREE STEPS, ONE BOW. The letters from Dharma Masters Heng Sure and Heng Ch'au chronicling the entirety of their 2 1/2 year journey to reach the City of 10,000 Buddhas. CHINESE only. $7.00.

HENG CH'AU'S JOURNAL - An account of the remarkable experiences and changes undergone by Bhikshu Heng Ch'au when he first became acquainted with Gold Mountain Monastery. $1.95.

OPEN YOUR EYES, TAKE A LOOK AT THE WORLD - The journals of Bhikshus Heng Sure and Heng Ch'au and Bhikshuni Heng Tao, taken during the 1978 Asia-region visit by the Ven. Abbot Hua together with other members of the Sino-American Buddhist Association. 347 pgs., 32-4, $7.50.

迷眼觀世界--亞州弘法記 - the above, in Chinese. 347 pgs., $7.50.

MUSIC, NOVELS, AND BROCHURES:

THREE CART PATRIARCH - A 12" stereo LP recorded by and for children, based on the Monkey Tales of China. $7.00 plus $1.00 shipping.

CITY OF 10,000 COLOR BROCHURE - Over 30 color photos of the center of World Buddhism located in the scenic Mendocino County near Wonderful Enlightenment Mountain. 24 pgs., $2.00.

CELEBRISI'S JOURNEY - David Round's novel describing the events in a modern American's quest for enlightenment. 178 pgs., 14-6, $4.00.

VAJRA BODHI SEA 萬佛城. A monthly journal of orthodox Buddhism published by the Sino-American Buddhist Association since 1970. Each issue contains the most recent translation work of the Buddhist Text Translation Society, as well as a biography of a great Patriarch of Buddhism from the ancient past, sketches of the lives of contemporary monastic and lay followers from around the world, a Sanskrit lesson, scholarly articles, and other material. The journal is BILINGUAL in Chinese and English in an 8 1/2" by 11" format. Single issues $2.00, one year $22.00, and three years $60.00.

POSTAGE AND HANDLING:

United States: $1.00 for the first book and 40¢ for each additional book. All publications are sent via special fourth class. Allow 4 days to 2 weeks for delivery.

International: $1.25 for the first book and 75¢ for each additional book. All publications are sent via "book rate." We recommend that for orders of approximately 10 or more, an additional $3.00 per parcel of 100 books be sent for registration to protect against loss. We are not responsible for parcels lost in the mail.

All orders require pre-payment before
they will be processed.

PUBLICATIONS AVAILABLE AT:

GOLD MOUNTAIN MONASTERY   (415) 861-9672
1731-15th Street
San Francisco, CA.   94103

THE CITY OF 10,000 BUDDHAS   (707) 462-0939
Box 217
Talmage, CA.   95481

GOLD WHEEL TEMPLE   (213) 483-7497
1728 West Sixth Street
Los Angeles, CA.   90017

中文佛書目錄

中美佛教總會法界大學出版

佛書部分：

①永嘉大師證道歌詮釋（全一冊）　美國萬佛城宣化上人講解　定價美金二元五角。

②緇門崇行錄　　蓮池大師著　弘一大師集　（贈閱）

③宣化上人偈讚闡釋錄（全一冊）　定價美金五元　（贈閱）

④宣化禪師事蹟（全一冊）　定價美金四元。

⑤放眼觀世界（亞洲弘法記）　（全一冊）　（贈閱）

⑥修行者的消息（三步一拜兩行者一心頂禮萬佛城之來鴻）　（贈閱）

⑦佛教精進者的日記　（平裝上冊）　定價美金六元。

⑧萬佛城雜誌月刊（漢英合刊）　定價一年美金二十二元。三年美金六十元。

即將出版：

①大方廣佛華嚴經淺釋（十定品至入法界品）

②楞嚴咒疏句偈解（漢英對照）　（第二冊）

③梵網經講錄（漢英對照）　（下冊）

④地藏菩薩本願經淺釋

⑤大佛頂首楞嚴經淺釋

⑥沙彌律儀淺釋

⑦佛教精進者的日記（下冊）

⑧宣化上人語錄

⑨萬佛城聯語集

總流通處：中美佛教總會金山寺

Gold mt. Monastery 1731 15th St. San Francisco, CA.94103 U.S.A.

經典部分：

①大方廣佛華嚴經序淺釋（漢英對照）　美國萬佛城宣化上人講解，全一冊。定價美金七元。

②大方廣佛華嚴經疏淺釋（平裝四冊）　美國萬佛城宣化上人講解。

第一冊（第一門，教起因緣）　定價美金五元。

第二冊（第二門，藏教所攝）　定價美金八元五角。

第三冊（第三門，義理分齊。第四門，教所被機。第五門，教體淺深。第六門，宗趣通別）

定價美金八元五角。

第四冊（第七門，部類品會。第八門，傳譯感通。第九門，總釋名題。第十門，別解文義）

定價美金五元。

③大方廣佛華嚴經淺釋（平裝八冊）　美國萬佛城宣化上人講解。

第一冊（世主妙嚴品第一，卷一至卷二）　定價美金七元。

第二冊（世主妙嚴品第一，卷三）　定價美金五元。

第三冊（世主妙嚴品第一，卷四至卷五）　定價美金七元。

第四冊（如來現相品第二。普賢三昧品第三。世界成就品第四）　定價美金五元。

第五冊（華藏世界品第五。毘盧遮那品第六。如來名號品第七。四聖諦品第八）

定價美金七元。

第六冊（光明覺品第九。菩薩問明品第十。淨行品第十一）　定價美金七元。

第七冊（賢首品第十二。升須彌山頂品第十三。須彌頂山偈讚第十四。十住品第十五）

定價美金七元。

第八冊（梵行品第十六。初發心功德品第十七。明法品第十八。升夜摩天品第十九。夜摩偈

讚品第二十）　定價美金五元。

南無阿彌陀佛

南無觀世音菩薩

南無大勢至菩薩

聖作行意教

三莫舉其佛

方惡善淨諸

西諸眾自是

④ 大方廣佛華嚴經十地品淺釋（平裝三冊） 美國萬佛城宣化上人講解。

第一冊（第一歡喜地） （漢英對照） 定價美金七元。

第二冊（第二離垢地。第三發光地。第四焰慧地。第五難勝地） 定價美金五元。

第三冊（第六現前地。第七遠行地。第八不動地。第九善慧地。第十法雲地）定價美金六元

⑤ 千手千眼大悲心陀羅尼經（全一冊） 定價美金六元。

⑥ 般若波羅蜜多心經非台頌解（全一冊） 美國萬佛城宣化上人講解 定價美金五元。

⑦ 楞嚴咒疏句偈解（漢英對照） （第一冊） 美國萬佛城宣化上人講解 定價美金八元五角。

⑧ 梵網經講錄（漢英對照） （上冊） 慧僧法師述 定價美金十元。